HAUNTED
LIVERPOOL 16

For Bethany Ireland

© Tom Slemen 2008

Published by The Bluecoat Press, Liverpool
Book design by March Graphic Design Studio, Liverpool
Printed by Ashford Colour Press

ISBN 1 904438 67 9

Tom Slemen

HAUNTED
LIVERPOOL 16

The Bluecoat Press

CONTENTS

SPINE-CHILLING POSSESSION

The following story was related to me by a nephew of the Mr Robinson character mentioned in the account. Without a doubt, there do exist accursed places on this planet, where strange and inexplicable things happen on a regular basis. These places are known as 'portals' – openings and gateways to unchartered realms inhabited by all sorts of terrifying beings.

One of these portals is thought to exist at a certain unassuming house within a stone's throw of Sefton Park. This house lay vacant in the early 1960s, but was illegally occupied by a Mr Robinson, a nasty small-time criminal in his fifties, who spent most of his time loafing about in the then squalid back parlour, quite warm and cosy, since he had managed to override the gas and electricity meters. He lived a rough but, to his mind, idyllic life there for a while; drinking heavily and bringing the occasional prostitute back to his squat via the back alleyway.

One afternoon, one such prostitute, by the name of Maria, had a terrifying experience at the dingy old house, whilst Robinson was out doing what he did best – stealing things that didn't belong to him. Maria later described how the nightmare had begun when she had suddenly noticed tall flames leaping out of the coal fire and out into the room. The flames were quickly followed by a thick cloud of choking black smoke and soot, which mushroomed out from the fireplace and settled in every nook and cranny and on to every inch of the sparse furniture in the room.

As the air slowly began to clear, a coughing and spluttering Maria, herself covered in the greasy soot from head to toe, watched in disbelief as a spine-chilling orange-skinned man with devilish horns, bat-like wings and red glowing eyes, appeared in the fireplace. At first, he was crouching on top of the hot coals, the heat from which didn't appear to be bothering him in the slightest. He then stepped out of the

fire and on to the hearth rug, where he straightened himself up and faced her. Maria felt sick and faint and as her legs started to give way and she noticed a much smaller version of the man – a second 'devil', with the same roasted earthenware skin, but this time just a few inches tall – flutter out of the fireplace to join his mate on the rug. The last thing Maria remembers was the sensation of blood draining from her head before she passed out.

When she came to, the little devils had gone and Robinson was standing over her, roughly demanding to know what had happened and why she was still there in his flat. The room, and everything in it, including Maria, was covered in a filthy film of soot and scattered coals. An old chair was lying splintered on its side and Maria's face was smarting from a series of deep scratches, which stood out livid red against her blackened skin. Her dress and blouse were torn to shreds and she looked a sorry sight.

Deeply traumatised, she tremblingly told Robinson what had happened, all the time nervously looking about her, as if she expected the demons to return at any moment. Robinson, being the kind of selfish man he was, was far more bothered about the state of 'his' home, than he was about poor Maria. He offered her no assistance whatsoever but instead angrily swore at her and told her to get out of his house. Despite still feeling very fragile, Maria gathered up her few possessions and gladly did just that.

That evening, having showered and changed into some other clothes, the prostitute was drinking in a pub on Park Road, when Robinson staggered in, looking completely deranged. He lurched over to the bar and faced Maria. His eyes bulged alarmingly, and he kept clutching at his throat, as if he were being strangled by invisible hands. He told Maria that "one of those things" – a little "devil" – had got inside him – apparently through his mouth! Maria gasped and backed away in revulsion.

"What shall I do?" he pleaded in desperation. "You saw them. What shall I do?"

"I'd go and find a priest if I was you, love," said Maria, feeling pleased that he had got his just deserts. "That dump you're living in's enough to give anyone the creeps. I still haven't recovered from last night. Me outfit's ruined and me nerves're in shreds," and turning to the barman she ordered another drink.

"I know … I'm sorry … I should've listened to …"

Robinson was unable to say another word as the horrible gurgling sound of his choking filled the pub, and people exchanged horrified glances as he started to foam heavily at the mouth.

"Oh my god!" said Maria, "The devils 'ave got 'im by the throat! Serves 'im right, though, the dirty swine!"

Robinson's eyes turned upwards into his forehead until only the whites were showing and, suddenly regaining the power of speech, he began laughing and screaming out the foulest obscenities. He was soon overpowered by the landlord with the help of some of his more burly customers and an ambulance was summoned. Still writhing like a thing possessed, he was taken to the Royal Hospital on Pembroke

Place, where he was put into an observation ward and firmly strapped to the bed, so that he couldn't harm himself, or others, when the 'fits' came on him.

On more than one occasion a young Irish nurse on night duty on that ward allegedly saw the thing that was possessing Robinson emerging from his mouth. Hospital wards can be very spooky and disturbing places in the middle of the night, especially for a young and inexperienced nurse and her story was quickly dismissed as an oversensitive reaction to the all pervading presence of death, which inevitably hung over the seriously ill patients, and which took some getting used to.

However, when Robinson suddenly and unexpectedly died of a brain haemorrhage a couple of nights later, a priest who had been carrying out the Last Rites on another patient, backed up the young nurse's story, when he testified to having seen something "unspeakably evil" flying out of the criminal's body as he passed away.

Robinson's sister arranged for him to be cremated at Anfield Crematorium, where members of staff allegedly noticed strange green sparks flying out of the incinerator as Robinson's body was being reduced to ash; something none of them had ever seen before.

I have done some research into the history of the house where Robinson was squatting, and it seems that, as far back as the late Edwardian period, the dwelling had already gained a supernatural reputation. Two suicides occurred at the house within a few years of each other, and in the 1970s, there were reports in the local press about a shadowy entity which roamed about from room to room, leaving behind a trail of icy cold air in its wake.

THE BLACK JESTER

In 1974, ten-year-old Tony Wesse was walking down Stanley Road, on his way home from school for his lunch. The time was around 12.10pm, and as he passed one of the streets off Stanley Road, he heard an old man shouting something across to him. Tony approached the bald old man who asked if he would be kind enough to go on an errand to the newsagents for him, to buy a newspaper and some sweets. He promised to give him "a few shillings" for his trouble. Excited by the prospect of getting his hands on some real money, Tony forgot all his mum and dad's dire warnings about strangers and followed the man into his home.

The oldster told him to wait in the parlour while he went to get the money for the errand. Several minutes passed by, and still the elderly stranger hadn't returned. Tony began to grow slightly anxious and shouted after him down the hallway and a faint voice replied, "I shan't be a minute. Just wait there, son."

The schoolboy looked around the rather gloomy room and suddenly noticed a tall column of shiny ten pence coins neatly stacked on top of the old dresser. Back in those days, the stack looked like a lot of money to a kid like Tony, whose parents never gave him any pocket money. He edged his way towards the dresser to get a closer look at the tempting pile and soon found the temptation too much. After glancing around guiltily, he grabbed the top half of the column in his fist and made a dash for it. But when when he opened the parlour door, the old man was standing there in the hallway, blocking his path – and he was brandishing a coiled leather belt in his hand. Gone was the look of helplessness and gone too was the kindly expression. He snarled and swore at Tony and grabbed him roughly by the collar of his school shirt.

"Gunna rob me, was you, yer little runt?"

Tony trembled from head to foot and shook his head. "N...n...no, mister. I was only lookin' ... honest to God."

"Lookin' me foot!" spat the old man, grabbing him by the arm and sending some of the filched coins scattering across the lino. He had a vice-like grip and formidable strength for someone of his age. "Shall I call the police, or should I punish you meself, hey?"

Tony felt sick and light-headed as adrenalin coursed through his veins, making every bit of his body throb painfully. He had to escape from this horrible man's clutches, but how? Then, with a sudden flash of inspiration, he pointed at the parlour window and shouted: "Hey! Look! There's me nan!"

The pensioner instinctively looked towards the window, upon which Tony threw the rest of the coins at the old man's face, and stooped down to make his getaway between his bony legs. He careered into the hall, heading for the front door, which was bolted, but he managed to unfasten the bolt before the old man was upon him.

"I know who you are, and where you live! Yer little villain. I'm callin' the police!" screeched the old man. "Don't think yer've got away with it. I'll see to that!"

But by this time Tony was halfway down the street, his stomach in tight little knots but his little legs working like pistons. He charged madly through street after street until he found himself in an unfamiliar neighbourhood, where, suddenly spotting a derelict house, he dived through a broken window. Once inside, he cowered in a dark corner, expecting the old man to come flying through the window at any moment. Several minutes went by in which nothing happened and Tony's breathing slowly returned to normal as his fear of capture gradually began to subside. Yet he still didn't dare move. He stayed in that house, afraid to go home, because he was convinced that the police would be waiting for him; waiting to lock him up …

At around 2pm an ominous gloom descended over the empty house, as the skies outside darkened and it started to rain heavily. Water started to come in through the numerous holes in the roof; the drips falling at different rates and creating eerie rhythms which reverberated through the empty house, giving Tony the creeps. He was desperate to go home and unburden himself to his mum, but he couldn't pluck up the courage. Suppose the police locked him up for a really long time – he might never see his friends again.

Tears were beginning to well up in his eyes, when suddenly the house began to echo to the strains of some ethereal music. It sounded like pipe music, and it was getting louder and louder by the second. Tony sat tight in the corner of the dusty old room, as he noticed the door slowly creaking open all by itself. He made himself as small as possible, in the hope that whatever it was would pass by without noticing him. Then, from the corner of his eye, he saw what can only be described as the silhouette of a jester entering the room, complete with pointed hat and footwear and playing some type of musical horn. Then, without warning, the sinister figure abruptly stopped playing his instrument and spun round to present a black featureless face to Tony.

The poor lad was terrified out of his wits. He shot up, and keeping his back to the wall and his eyes pinned to the sinister silhouette, he inched his way along the cobweb-strewn wall towards the open window. The minute he reached the broken pane he flung himself out on to the pavement. Luckily, the window was on the ground floor, so he didn't hurt himself too badly, just a few cuts and bruises, nothing broken. He pelted down the deserted street, too scared to look back at the weird apparition, and he soon found his bearings again after coming across a familiar road.

When he reached home, he felt he had to tell someone about his day's traumatic events and he chose his gran, judging, quite rightly, that she would be the least likely to punish him and the most likely to believe his story and perhaps even show him a bit of sympathy.

"What on earth's the matter, pet?" said his gran, when she saw his battered knees, and his jumper all covered in dust and cobwebs and mould. "You look like you've been pulled through a hedge backwards. Come on, you know you can tell me. What's up?"

"Oh! gran, I've had a horrible time. Yer goin' to be dead angry with me when I tell yer," sobbed Tony, sinking his head into his gran's ample bosom.

"Don't be so daft!" You know you can tell yer old gran anything," said his gran, pulling the filthy jumper over his head. "You just sit down over there and while I make a cup of tea and clean up those knees, you can tell me all about it."

So while his gran fussed round him, Tony stammered out his sorry tale. He had decided that it was best to tell her everything that had happened, including the bit he was really ashamed of – stealing the money – so he was surprised by her reaction. Rather than the good telling off that he was expecting, his gran told him that the old man who had accused him of stealing had pulled the same trick before. He would invite a child into his house under some trumped up pretext and then tempt him by leaving money out on the dresser. He would then peep through a hole in the wall until he saw the boy fall for the bait, and then he'd catch him red-handed and ask him if he should call the police, or thrash him with his belt. Apparently, the old man was known by the community to be a sadist and only that month had been arrested for perpetrating his sick tricks.

After he had listened to this explanation, he then had to listen to a lecture from his gran about not talking to strangers and not taking things which don't belong to you etc etc, but he thought it was a small price to pay; after all, he could only blame himself for getting into the mess in the first place. Like most things, as time went by the incident began to fade in his memory, until eventually it had lost all its terror.

However, eight years later, in 1982, Tony was to be reminded of that day from his childhood when he met a girl at a dance and asked if he could walk her home. The street in which she lived looked all too familiar to Tony and he quickly recognised it as the one he had run to when escaping from the old trickster. In fact, the girl lived directly opposite the house where Tony had hidden on that fateful day when he was a ten-year-old schoolboy; the house where he had seen that uncanny jester. Amazingly, the house was still vacant and his girlfriend told him that it had always remained vacant because it was known to be haunted by a medieval-looking ghost in a pointed hat. Neighbours had often heard spine-chilling laughter coming from that empty house at all hours of the day and night.

Just why a medieval ghost should still be haunting a perfectly ordinary Kirkdale house remains a mystery. If anyone has any enlightening suggestions, please write or email me with your views. My contact details are given in the back pages of this book.

DEVIL IN THE ELEVATOR

Whenever Christmas comes nigh, I frequently get asked to tell a traditional Yuletide ghost story, and I have many of them in my repertoire, but I also have other seasonal supernatural tales that are not only far from traditional, but are also downright terrifying. One such tale was reported to me in 2007, and involved a young lecturer from a certain university. For the purposes of this story, we shall call this man Tim.

Tim is a decent enough fellow, and I have known him for a few years. He used to be a zealous atheist, an enemy of superstition and anything connected with the paranormal; a man who firmly believed that God did not exist. He used to take great delight in repeatedly telling me that ghosts were either optical illusions, or figments of overactive imaginations. He believed that death was the end for all human beings and that there was no afterlife beyond burial or cremation. He was a great fan of Richard Dawkins, the popular science writer and evolutionary biologist, who recently wrote the sensational, if controversial, bestseller *The God Delusion*, which unequivocally postulates that a Divine Creator does not exist and that all religions are therefore delusional.

Just before Christmas Eve, 2007, Tim visited Liverpool city centre and spent almost an hour in Starbucks café, arguing over a cup of coffee with a friend named Chris, who had once also been an atheist but had recently altered his views and become a believer in a divine creator since the birth of his first child. Chris was attempting to explain to his cynical friend why he had undergone such a dramatic change of heart, but Tim was not prepared to listen to any opposing viewpoints.

Finally, in exasperation, he said, "Look, mate, I'm telling you, God does not exist. Okay? In fact, I challenge him to strike me dead in fifteen seconds if I'm wrong."

Chris held his breath, but fifteen seconds came and went and nothing happened and Tim was still sitting there looking smug, when an old man who had been listening in to the argument from a nearby table came over and presented Tim with a trick question.

"Excuse me interrupting, but I overheard you knocking God just then. If God does not exist, then the Devil does not exist either ... is that right?"

Tim grinned. He'd heard it all before and there was nothing he liked better than a good old fashioned argument, especially one about religion. He nodded, saying, "Yeah, that's right, mate. There is no good or bad ..."

Upon which the elderly man raised his hand and said, "Alright then, if there is no Devil, can he have your soul?"

Tim smiled uneasily and replied, "No, because I don't have a soul and there is no Devil."

"Well, in that case, you won't object to giving your soul to him then?" said the man.

Tim repeated his arguments over and over again until finally, to get rid of the old man who had started to annoy him, he said, "Look, okay. If the Devil exists ... and I believe he doesn't ... but if he does ... then he's welcome to my soul. Satisfied?"

The old man made no reply but just walked out of the premises without a word.

Listening to the conversation had left Chris feeling deeply troubled and fearful for his friend, with whom he pleaded to relent and think again. "Tim, tell God you've changed your mind and say you're sorry, for goodness sake."

Tim resolutely shook his head and tried to smile, but all his old reassurance had suddenly deserted him. He frowned and seemed troubled himself, as if he were having doubts about his atheistic convictions for the first time.

"Look, this is getting boring. Let's change the subject," he said. "Do you fancy another coffee?"

"No, I'd better get going, I'm sure there'll be nappies to change back home. But seriously, Tim, please think about what I've said. I'm really worried about you."

The two men soon parted on Bold Street, each going their separate ways, each with their beliefs still intact. Chris went home to his wife and new baby and Tim set off for the John Lewis retail store near Clayton Square. He went up to the top floor and bought several items, and then summoned the elevator with the press of a button to take him back down to the ground floor. When the doors opened, there was already one person inside. Tim assumed that he was going to step out of the elevator, as he had obviously ridden it up to the top floor, but the man – who had dark, swept-back receding hair and a Van Dyke beard – stayed put. Tim stepped into the elevator and said to the man, who was standing next to the buttons, "Ground floor, please".

The stranger pressed the right button, the doors closed, and down they went, but when the elevator reached the ground floor it didn't stop, as it should have done, but kept on going. Tim realised that it had overshot the ground floor and was now going to the basement, and he shook his head and tutted in annoyance. But the elevator didn't stop at the basement either. He could feel it accelerating, plunging faster and faster and faster out of control, the free-fall sensation made his stomach churn and his head feel light.

People in lifts invariably avoid making eye contact with the other occupants. They even avoid looking in the direction of any of the other passengers, such is human etiquette when people find themselves in a confined space with total strangers. But now Tim deliberately turned to look at the other person in the lift, hoping for some explanation or reassurance but instead, he saw, to his utter amazement, that the man had acquired a pair of horns.

"That's right!" smirked the man, who was obviously the Devil, as he stared back at Tim, his face the personification of evil.

An unbearable suffocating heat then began to pervade the free-falling elevator, and, struggling to breathe, Tim quickly sank to his knees and passed out in a crumpled heap in a corner of the elevator. When he came round he was surrounded by concerned customers and staff from the store.

After that spine-chilling experience, Tim became so afraid of having another encounter with Satan, that he took up residence in a Catholic priest's house for a fortnight. He still hasn't made a full recovery from his sobering ordeal; an ordeal which forced him to question his long held beliefs.

When he related his story to me, I watched as the goosebumps erupted on his arms, a sure sign of the validity of the tale, and one which is far more reliable than the readings from any lie-detecting polygraph.

BIRTH OMENS

Over the years I have collected many strange accounts of women who became pregnant after undergoing some kind of paranormal experience and here are just a couple of these controversial but fascinating cases.

The Song of Bernadette

One rainy Sunday afternoon in the early 1970s, forty-two-year-old Celia was feeling lonely and depressed because she had recently split up with Jimmy, her partner of ten years, after catching him red handed him with a girl in his arms one night, when she walked into the Vines pub on Lime Street. She had not been prepared to listen to what she described as his feeble excuses and had packed her bags that night and flounced out of the house, slamming the door behind her. Since the split, Celia had been living with her widowed mother on the Radcliffe Estate in Everton.

She missed Jimmy terribly and felt that she no longer had anything left to live for. She slumped down in an armchair on that gloomy afternoon after the usual heavy Sunday dinner that was traditional at her mother's house. She had never liked the tedious routine of Sundays – all the shops were shut in those days and there was nothing to do, and now she found them even more difficult to cope with. With just her elderly mother for company and the ticking of the clock the only noise in the claustrophobic sitting room, time dragged by and Celia felt totally trapped and that life was passing her by.

After a while, her boredom and frustration lulled her into a fitful doze – the wretched black cloud of depression ever present, even during sleep. She had been dozing like this for some time when, without warning, some music coming from the record player startled her awake. A single disc was on the turntable, which she quickly identified as 'Bernadette', by the Four Tops. Celia had not played that record in years, in fact she had forgotten that she still had it and she knew that her mother wouldn't have dreamt of putting it on, she was a technophobe and never even touched the record player. So she looked at the vinyl disc in disbelief as it revolved on the turntable, and a host of memories came flooding back.

But who on earth could have switched the record player on? Celia just could not fathom it out and quickly realised that there were forces at work in that room that she did not understand. Then events took an even spookier turn, because when she switched on the television, there on the screen was a film starring Jennifer Jones, entitled *The Song of Bernadette*. Celia switched off the record player and settled down to watch the film, which was just beginning. It was about the peasant girl Bernadette, who had seen the Virgin Mary appear to her at Lourdes, in south west France.

The next morning, Celia woke up feeling queasy and generally not herself. She skipped breakfast and the nausea gradually subsided as the day wore on, but the next morning she woke up feeling just as bad again. The sickness lasted for about a week, after which time she became worried and went to see her doctor – and discovered that she was pregnant. She had been suffering from classic morning sickness but in her depressed state had not made the connection. A succession of conflicting emotions overwhelmed her – joy that she was pregnant, but despair that she no longer had a partner with whom to share that joy. She wished that she could turn the clocks back and be with Jimmy once again; they had been so happy together until that night …

Celia was just getting used to the idea of becoming a single mother, when a repentant Jimmy came to find her at mother's house clutching a large bouquet of red roses. As soon as Celia opened the door to him he thrust the roses into her hands and got down on his knees and earnestly begged her forgiveness, saying that he had only been flirting with the girl after having a few drinks. Okay, he knew that it was wrong, but nothing had happened and it was Celia that he loved, and always would.

Celia didn't hesitate for a moment and fell into his arms. She was back where she belonged. Later that night she revealed to him that she was pregnant, and a delighted Jimmy rushed out as soon as the shops were open the next day and made straight for the nearest jeweller's. He bought an engagement ring, then rushed back to Celia and asked her to marry him. Celia gave him the answer he was looking for and after they had embraced, Jimmy made a strange request, "If it's a girl, could we call her Bernadette?" Celia was completely taken aback by the series of apparent coincidences involving that name, but readily agreed to the name. Although she felt that something peculiar was going on, which she didn't understand, she was confident that that something, was good.

Nine months later she gave birth to a beautiful baby girl, whom she and Jimmy called Bernadette.

The Rose Girl

One serene evening in the summer of 1965, twenty-four-year-old Christine was sitting in her flat on Huskisson Street, sipping tea whilst idly gazing out of the open window. Sitting alongside her was her elderly neighbour, Maude, also drinking tea. A spectacular sunset had gilded the street with a soft patina of old gold. The scene was made even more memorable because, for once, the street was completely deserted, not a soul was about, not even a dog or cat.

"Looks really lovely, doesn't it, Maude?" said Christine, topping up her neighbour's cup of tea.

"It does, dear – a real picture."

As they carried on enjoying the scene, the two women became aware of what they would later describe as some "dreamy waltz

music" floating distantly in the air. At the same time, the stillness of
the scene was suddenly broken by the sight of an oddly-dressed lone
figure making its way down Huskisson Street. As the figure drew
closer it was clear that it was a girl; a girl with blonde hair and aged
no more than about nine or ten. She was wearing an old fashioned
black straw bonnet and a knee-length navy blue dress. In her hand she
was carrying what seemed to be some kind of wreath fashioned out of
pink roses. She suddenly came to a halt and hung this rose-garland on
the railings fronting a certain house. Having completed her mission
with no obvious ceremony, the girl simply turned around and walked
back to where she had come from – and, along with the spectral music
– she gradually faded from sight.

The two women watched the curious episode in stunned silence.
Only after the child had finally disappeared did Christine turn to look

at her friend, whose shocked expression matched her own. Maude was also solemnly making the sign of the cross.

"You know what we've just seen, don't you, dear?" she asked, knowingly.

"So you saw it too! Yes. I couldn't believe my eyes, Maude. Do you think she was a ghost or something?"

"Yes, of course, dear. You've just seen the 'Rose Girl'," said Maude in a surprisingly matter-of-fact way. "She's been seen in this street for I don't know how many years and she always leaves a wreath in front of a house where a special child is to be born."

Any scepticism which Christine may have felt was soon dispelled when she found out that a forty-four-year-old, supposedly infertile, woman had discovered that she was pregnant shortly after finding the pink wreath on the railings in front of her house. She had given up all hope of ever becoming a mother and both she and her doctors regarded her pregnancy as nothing short of miraculous.

I had already heard about this ghost myself, even before hearing of Christine's account. This was through my mother, who had a friend called Betty who also lived on Huskisson Street and who had seen the phantom child herself years before. On that occasion – a cold wintry morning back in 1962 – it had been snowing heavily, and Betty was preparing to go to work. She had wrapped up warmly and put on her Wellingtons and as she opened the door at 7 o'clock, she took in the pristine sight of the newly fallen snow which had transformed her street and the city into a winter wonderland and took several deep breaths of pure pleasure. Mornings like this made her feel glad to be alive and she was looking forward to her walk to work.

She set off down Huskisson Street and immediately thought it odd when she came upon a child trudging through the blanket of deep snow carrying what she assumed to be a wreath of holly and ivy, at that early hour of the morning. Betty watched as the child carefully placed the wreath on the spikes of the railings outside the house where her cousin Donna lived. Out of curiosity, Betty tramped along the snowy pavement towards the girl, who suddenly began to walk away from the railings – then eerily vanished into thin air before she was able to get close to her.

Betty knew immediately that she had seen a phantasm, because the child had not left a single footprint in the snow. But the wreath was still there. Betty decided that it was best not to touch the wreath of what turned out to be roses, which she noticed were of the same delicate bridal pink as the dress in which she had been wedded the year before. Suddenly noticing that the time was getting on, she then continued on her way to work, all the time pondering the significance of the wreath and the ghostly girl. Betty had not talked to her cousin Donna for almost two years, all because of a silly argument over nothing, and for that reason she decided not to tell her about the ghostly goings-on in front of her house.

So, imagine her surprise when, about a fortnight later, she received a letter from Donna, right out of the blue. Her cousin had just discovered that she was pregnant, and wanted to share the good news with Betty. Deciding to let bygones be bygones, Betty went over to her cousin's house and they hugged one another and said they were sorry, then Betty put on the kettle. Donna then announced that she would like Betty to be the godmother to the new baby. Betty was delighted and flattered by the offer and gladly accepted, saying that it would be an honour and a privilege. The two cousins then sat for hours excitedly chatting and making plans for the forthcoming event, their silly quarrel consigned to history.

In the course of the conversation, Betty mentioned the ghostly girl and the rose wreath that she had left on the railings in front of her door, which made Donna's eyes widen. She had certainly found the peculiar but beautifully-made garland on that snowy winter's day, and had wondered who could possibly have put it there. Donna was naturally unsettled by Betty's ghostly account, and later that day repeated the tale to an elderly neighbour, Mrs Jerome, who told Donna that the Rose Girl, as the ghost was known locally, had haunted that street since Victorian times, and was believed to be the phantom of a child named Ruby, who had once belonged to a wealthy family on Huskisson Street.

Young Ruby was said to have died from a fever when still a child and her ghost was first seen roaming about the street not long after her death. She and her mother used to make wreaths and artificial flower decorations for a living, and while she worked, Ruby used to always talk about having a large family when she grew up, because she adored children, especially babies. Her ghost was also said to occasionally haunt nearby Bedford and Egerton Streets.

After her initial alarm had died down, Donna liked the story; it made her feel that her pregnancy was even more special and when she later gave birth to a baby girl, she even decided to call her Rose – to acknowledge the part played in her birth by the enchanting and mysterious ghost of the little Rose Girl.

BEWARE OF THE BOGEYMAN

The 'bogeyman' – that vague folkloric character, of which successive generations of children live in fear and trepidation – comes in many shapes and forms and is usually explained away as a rather cynical tool used by parents to control their children's behaviour. In particular, the bogeyman is most often used to stop children from going to places which their parents deem unsafe – "Don't go there or the bogeyman'll get you," was certainly a warning which was regularly given to previous generations of children, although many of today's children are lucky if they get past the front door! The parents issuing these warnings never went into details, so it was left to the children's imaginations to decide what this bogeyman might look like, or do to them. Sometimes, however, the bogeyman has turned out to be only too real and is even capable of giving adults a nasty shock, never mind the children.

In February 1958, three thirteen-year-old school friends, Roger, Danny and Jimmy, were playing about near some ponds on farmland near Clough Road in Speke, at around 4.30pm in the afternoon, oblivious to their mothers' dire warnings about not going to the fields because of the 'bogeyman'. At thirteen, they all laughed at such warnings and took absolutely no notice of their mothers; that bogeyman stuff was just for kids.

Twilight was falling fast and the last glimmers of the thin daylight were just disappearing over the western horizon, when all three lads were stopped in their tracks as a long white object was spotted floating across the marshy ground in the distance. Time seemed to stand still as they watched the apparition make an abrupt turn and then come hovering over towards them. It was like nothing they had ever seen before, but as the nebulous form came closer and closer, it soon became recognisable as a giant human male figure, at least ten feet in height. The massive oval head was somewhat obscured by a pale blue hood and the figure was swathed in a long robe of the same colour.

Roger was the last of the boys to gather his wits together and run off, so he was the one who was able to see at close quarters that the ghost had a long black moustache and a swarthy face. The eyes of the elongated phantom were set abnormally wide apart, even in relation to its size, and they glared threateningly at Roger, who suddenly came to his senses and turned on his heels and sped off home without once daring to take a single backward glance.

Each of the boys told his parents about the colossal spectre, expecting them to call the police, or the local newspapers, or at the very least offer them some comforting words, but not one of them took them seriously. The parents' general reaction was to just laugh and wink at each other and make sarcastic comments such as, "That's what you get when you play in places like that, we've told you often enough," or, "How many times have we told you the bogeyman'd get you if you played in those fields? Now, perhaps, you'll do as you're told for once".

So the apparition was dismissed by the adults as an imaginary bogeyman, a childish fiction. The lads had probably seen the mist falling on the fields and making weird shapes, and then imagined all the rest. Whatever they had seen, it had given them a bit of a fright and, hopefully, it would teach them a lesson and they would stay away from the fields in future. However, boys will be boys, and so that was not to be the end of this intriguing story.

Despite their unpleasant experience, the children's inquisitiveness soon got the better of them and after a short lapse, they began to rendezvous once again on the farmland adjacent to Clough Road each night after school. Once there, they would encounter the ghost more often than not, but they never stuck around long enough to let it get close to them. However, familiarity breeds contempt, as they say, and after a while the boys began to feel a bit more blasé about the ghost. What harm could it do them anyway?

And so it was that, one afternoon, Danny, suddenly feeling brave and wanting to show off in front of his mates, foolishly decided to start throwing stones at the ghost. It was an action that he quickly regretted. He had just thrown the first stone when the hooded spectre reacted by wheeling round and accelerating towards him and his two friends with lightning speed.

As the ghost shot towards them in a straight line, like a ghostly guided missile, Roger and Jimmy managed to scramble off over the even ground, which was swampy from the recent heavy rainfall, but Danny was less fortunate. He slipped on a wet tussock of grass, lost his footing, and plunged face-first into three feet of freezing muddy pond water. When he looked up, the ghost was towering above him like some creature from a horror movie, but this was real life and the fear he felt was more intense than anything he had ever felt in his life. The ghost's olive-coloured face was contorted into an expression of pure hatred, as it slowly opened its cavernous snake-like jaws and bellowed something unintelligible in a deep and thunderous voice, which echoed around the deserted fields and made Danny's eardrums painfully vibrate. His legs felt like they didn't belong to him any more, and yet he somehow managed to crawl away for a short distance before scrambling to his feet and then pelting back across the fields. He vaulted over walls and stiles with an athleticism he didn't even know he had, with the ghost howling like a banshee, hard on his heels.

Danny doesn't know to this day how he managed to escape from the ghost's clutches, but somehow he did. This time when he staggered through the front door of his home drenched to the bone and covered in mud and with a face the colour of putty, his mum and dad were a little less cynical and exchanged anxious looks as he described the events of that terrible afternoon. Indeed, the three boys' stories were corroborated only a week later, when several adults witnessed for themselves the tall apparition gliding over the same piece of farmland as they were on their way to work one morning. Scarcely able to comprehend what they were seeing, they traced the ghost's progress until it vanished into the early morning mist.

After that episode the phantom made itself scarce and has not been seen since, and no one has been able to establish whose ghost it was. One plausible suggestion that was put forward was that it was the ghost of the Child of Hale – a local giant of a man by the name of John Middleton, who had stood at an astounding nine feet and three inches in height in his stockinged feet when he was alive, nearly five hundred years ago. He was born in the village of Hale in 1578, and a full-length portrait of him hangs in Speke Hall to this day and a pub in the village is called after him.

ROAD RAGE

A more modern bogeyman, of sorts, was reportedly at large in Liverpool in the early 1970s. A flamboyant character dressed in a distinctive black velvet suit and with a long black cape lined with red satin was often reported driving recklessly across the city, deliberately trying to run children down in his flashy red 1963 Jaguar E Type sports car. From the numerous accounts I have received about this evil eccentric, who apparently sported a mop of white curly hair, and had a very large nose, he had an uncanny knack of appearing out of nowhere and then vanishing just as mysteriously when motorists tried to give chase after one of his exploits.

He was first encountered on Toxteth's Princes Road in 1972, where he chased a terrified group of children and a teenager for no apparent reason. They made their escape, but the madman returned an hour later, this time right inside the gates of Princes Park itself, where he almost succeeded in mowing down two girls who were innocently strolling down one of the leafy avenues.

One evening, two days later, he was spotted tearing down Oxford Street and Mount Pleasant at an outrageous speed and swerving from one side of the road to the other, with absolutely no thought for other road users or pedestrians. Indeed, an eleven-year-old boy was forced to scramble up the railings of Abercromby Park, when the red Jaguar came careering towards him along the pavement, apparently bent on killing him.

The next two encounters with the mad motorist took place outside the Busman's Social Club on Picton Road, and also on a secluded lane near Childwall Golf Club. Stephen Hall, a Tuebrook resident who drove buses in the 1970s, clearly remembers coming across the menacing red Jaguar in 1973. Stephen was driving the Number 26 bus up Sheil Road one summer evening at around 8.40pm, when he saw a red car come hurtling towards him on the wrong side of the road. The busman slammed on his brakes and braced himself for what he was certain was going to be the inevitable impact. In the event, the red Jaguar swerved at the very last second, over on to the right side of the road. As it rocketed past, Stephen and several of his shocked passengers managed to get a good view of the maniac, and took particular note of his cape fluttering in the air behind him. About a minute later, the Jaguar screeched back on to the scene, and made a sharp turn down Hampstead Road, where it narrowly missed a gang of children playing a game of street football.

On the following night two police mini panda cars were seen chasing the psychopathic driver down Judge's Drive, Newsham Park, but the officers of the law were unable to catch up with the caped crackpot, and he escaped by accelerating down West Derby Road at a suicidal speed, which they estimated to be in the region of 150 miles per hour.

The man in the red car was next seen suicidally driving down a narrow back alleyway on Lawrence Road between Blantyre and Avondale Roads, in August 1973. On that occasion the Jaguar ran over and crushed the bike of a nine-year-old child, whose irate father, cabdriver Rob Johnson, chased the sports car in his taxi as far as Woodlands Road in Aigburth, in what became a treacherous cat and mouse game. Rob believes that the demented driver was well-to-do and lived in a certain mansion in Aigburth, as he is almost sure he saw the Jaguar darting into the sweeping driveway of a palatial house in the area. When Rob followed him up to the gates of the house in question, they closed automatically, barring his way.

In another sighting, Eddie, a retired policeman, was patrolling down Toxteth's Park Road one Sunday in early 1974, when he spotted an outlandishly dressed man standing on the corner of Warwick Street, apparently having an altercation with an elderly black man. The former was about five feet seven inches in height, with white curly hair. He was also wearing the characteristic long black cloak and

31

debonair black velvet suit described by other witnesses and this time also had a red silk scarf tied loosely around his neck to complete the flamboyant outfit. Parked close by was a beautiful red gleaming car that the policeman instantly recognised as a 1963 E Type Jaguar.

Upon seeing Eddie approaching slowly in the police car, the well-dressed man reacted immediately. He ran in a sprightly manner over to his car and hopped into the driving seat without opening the door. Eddie watched helplessly as he tore off at an incredible speed in the direction of Upper Parliament Street. Eddie believes the engine in the Jaguar must have been souped-up in some way, because of the way the vehicle accelerated so dramatically as it reached Smithdown Road. The Jaguar wove in and out of the traffic at a phenomenal speed and yet managed to avoid the other vehicles on the road. Although Eddie radioed police headquarters to alert them to the antics of the devil-driver, the crazed dandy once again managed to evade capture.

The reports of this crazy and utterly reckless driver's exploits came in less and less frequently until they ceased altogether. He was last seen bulleting out of the city down the East Lancashire Road with his cape and red scarf billowing out behind him. Maybe it was intended to be a one-way journey, or perhaps his luck had finally run out and he crashed and died somewhere on the cold macadam of the Northwest's motorways. Some believe he was never alive in the first place, but was a ghost of the road, a theory which would certainly help to explain why he was never caught ...

THE TALISMAN

Moonrise took place at around 5.30pm on Thursday 23 March 1978, and was casually witnessed by thirteen-year-old Samantha, as she walked her family's dog through the Black Wood in Woolton. Sam's family only lived a short distance away from the wood, on Druid's Cross Road, and it was her job to take the family dog for its daily exercise.

On this particular windy evening Sam came upon a boy of her own age using a metal detector. He was sweeping over the ground within the wood with long even movements and was so absorbed in what he was doing that he didn't notice Sam until she had walked right up to him. The two got talking, and Sam soon learned that the boy's name was Michael, and that he lived on nearby Cuckoo Lane. Michael told her that he wanted to go to university to become an archaeologist when he left school, and he showed her a couple of the things he had unearthed locally: an unidentified coin from Childwall Woods and a small blackened metallic disc, about four inches in diameter, with Runic-type symbols etched upon it, which he had found nestling amongst some old gnarled tree roots in the Black Wood.

Sam took the disc from him and held it in the palm of her hand. She turned it this way and that and finally said that it would make an attractive pendant. Michael, being rather enamoured with the pretty girl, told her she could keep the disc and use it as a good luck talisman, even though he was very proud of his find and really wanted to keep it for himself.

The two young people felt very comfortable in each other's company and stood chatting there for quite a while, until Sam's father came running up to them through the wood. It was obvious that he had been worrying about Sam and he asked her why she had been out so long, her mother was worried stiff. Sam was surprised to learn that the time was already 6.40pm and apologised to her father, before saying goodbye to her new friend.

That evening, Samantha carefully washed the disc and studied the mysterious graven symbols upon it, but they were indecipherable, at least to her untrained eye. Her father drilled a hole through the disc and her mother threaded a small silver chain through it. As she did so, Sam confided in her and told her about Michael and how interesting he was, so different from the boys in her class who were so immature and silly, especially around girls. Sam's mother smiled to herself, realising that her daughter was growing up and had obviously formed a romantic attachment to this boy Michael, and she suggested bringing him round to the house some time in the near future.

That night, Sam was reading her *Jackie* magazine in bed when she fell asleep in the middle of one of the stories. She woke up at about one o'clock in the morning, and reached over to switch off her bedside lamp. A dazzling full moon was shining into her room, illuminating everything with a beautiful but rather ghostly light. She was just snuggling under the covers, when she heard a creaking sound coming from somewhere to the left of her and she looked across the room to see the reassuring thin line of bright yellow from the landing light shining under her door.

She was just about to turn over and go back to sleep, when two dark shapes suddenly broke up that line; someone must be standing right outside the door.

"Mum, is that you?" Sam called out in a weak voice. The feet visible through the crack under the door moved slightly. Sam called out again, "Mum ... answer me ... please ... is that you?"

This time the feet moved slowly away. She got out of bed and inched open the door to find no one there. She crept along the landing to her parents' bedroom and looked in on them. They were both sound asleep and she decided not to wake them. It was probably nothing, just her imagination, she reasoned to herself, although, deep down she was not so sure.

Sam nervously returned to her room, jumped into bed and quickly cocooned herself inside her duvet. She felt for Michael's 'talisman' on the chain around her neck and prayed that it would protect her from whatever had been lurking outside her room, if indeed there had been anything. She had closed her eyes for no more than a minute when, suddenly, there came an insistent tapping at the window. She peeked over the top of the duvet and was confronted by the stuff nightmares – a deathly pale gaunt face was peeping in at her. The eyes of this entity, which seemed to be hovering just outside the window, were black and hollow and as it smiled it revealed a set of truly terrifying pointed fangs.

Samantha rolled off her bed and stumbled towards the door. She ran out of her room and into her parents' bedroom where her screams instantly startled them awake. Whilst her mother comforted her, Sam's father went to her bedroom but could see no face at the window. However, on closer inspection, he did notice that a pane of glass had been cracked.

Samantha was naturally reluctant to sleep in her bed again after that night, and whenever she did, she suffered the most gruelling nightmares featuring the chalk-white sinister face peering in at her through the bedroom window, full of menace. Her mother and father did everything they could to try and reassure their daughter that she had merely dreamt that she had seen the 'vampire' and, for over a month, things settled down and Sam thankfully saw nothing out of the ordinary. She gradually came to accept her parents' version of events, the common sense version, they argued. Although she still had problems explaining how her window had come to be cracked, if the thing she had seen on that first night had just been something out of a bad dream.

By late April of that year, Michael had become Sam's boyfriend, and one afternoon, he asked her to go 'night-camping' with him. Sam initially refused, knowing that her parents would be horrified if they found out, because she hated doing things behind their backs. But Michael was very persuasive, constantly begging her to do it until he finally wore her down and she agreed. She sneaked out of her house at 2 o'clock in the morning and Michael was waiting for her outside equipped with a tent and a rucksack full of things they would need for their adventure.

They set off to put up their tent on the aptly-named Camp Hill, one of the area's oldest beauty spots, and a popular place for picnics and walks. However, little did the two teens realise that the night they had chosen to camp out – 30 April – was Hexennacht, the night that had been traditionally celebrated by witches and warlocks for centuries.

By 2.55am, the tent had been erected, if somewhat wonkily, and the clandestine pair sat huddled together inside on a ground-sheet and some folded blankets. The only light was provided by a dangerous-looking old paraffin lamp and the dim beam of light from the lamp on the front of Michael's Chopper bike. Michael was just about to say something romantic when he and Sam heard distant voices, followed by a diffused orange light shining through the tent fabric from outside. They peeped out of the tent and saw a large fire with a circle of silhouetted people standing around it, about sixty yards away. One of these individuals stood on the other side of the fire, and by the light of the flames, Sam could plainly see that he had the same pale face and

ghastly features as the man who had stared through her bedroom window over a month back. He wore a long cape, as black as the rest of his garments, and they both estimated his height to be well over six foot. This pallid-faced ghoul suddenly pointed at the tent and said something to the other shadowy figures. This seemed to be the signal for them to come running en masse towards Sam and Michael.

The two teenagers abandoned the tent at once and ran hell for leather down Camp Hill in a state of extreme terror. Sam looked back over her shoulder, just for a second, and saw about twelve people racing after them, along with a huge black growling dog that looked even more massive than a Great Dane and twice as aggressive. As their pursuers closed in on them, Sam somehow sensed a connection between them and her talisman. She wrenched it off her neck chain and threw it behind her. Her hunch was absolutely right, because almost immediately the band of menacing people and the mammoth hound ceased giving chase.

Sam and Michael were deeply shaken by their adventure that had gone so badly wrong. Night after night in the ensuing months, they suffered identical graphic nightmares involving human sacrifices being performed on Camp Hill. No one has ever been able to explain who the caped man was, nor the object of that bonfire ritual on Camp

Hill, and to date, nor has anyone ever managed to decipher the symbols on that black disc unearthed in Black Wood. Sam copied the symbols on the disc into her school exercise book but they meant nothing to her, or to anyone else.

Camp Hill has been the scene of numerous hauntings and strange sights over the years. In the late Bronze Age (and probably the early Iron Age) there was a hill fort at the summit of Camp Hill, although virtually no evidence of this ancient fortress still exists today. There was some dry-stone walling evident as late as the 1950s atop Camp Hill, but this was excavated, and landscaping of the hill by the park planners swept away the ancient earthworks that formed part of the hilltop fortress. See *Haunted Liverpool 14* for the sinister old tale of the 'Sunday King' – a vagrant and his associates who, so the dark legend goes, were transmogrified into a king and his courtiers every Sunday in return for forfeiting their souls to the Devil. For decades, a long white illuminated tent, about fifty feet in length, has been seen on Camp Hill, with silhouettes of people milling about within it, but the tent's purpose and the identity of the shadowy people within, also remains a mystery.

There is another strange phenomenon concerning Camp Hill that has been mentioned to me on several occasions. Motorists driving down Hillfoot Road and School Lane have experienced an intense and unsettling feeling that someone, or something, is in the back of their vehicles. These two roads run on either side of Camp Hill, and even people walking or jogging past this area have perceived an ominous presence following closely behind them.

In my own opinion, Camp Hill is one of the many 'window areas' of this planet – specific zones that have a high incidence of paranormal activity such as ghost and even UFO sightings. If you are in search of a paranormal experience, then Camp Hill should be top of your list for a visit, but if possible do not go alone; you never know what you might find …

THE HEALING THREAD

The following riveting tale was derived from a story in an exceedingly rare Edwardian book of supernatural mysteries entitled *Strange Gleanings*, written by Messrs Sherrard and Fenner, and published by Duckworth & Co, of Henrietta Street, London, in 1910. I found the old leather-bound volume whilst browsing in a quaint second-hand Renshaw Street bookshop that unfortunately was bulldozed a few years ago.

One early golden spring evening in 1906, the Williams family of Mornington Terrace – a row of fine Georgian houses on Upper Liverpool's Duke Street – was entertaining a Mr and Mrs Salter of Islington, when an old woman knocked on the door to the servant's entrance. This occurred just as high tea was being served upstairs in the dining room. The superstitious Welsh butler Mr Lewis answered the door and was confronted by a shrivelled old Romany woman who carried a basket crammed with flowers, herbs, charms and suchlike. Her name was Mrs Bell, an occasional clandestine visitor to the house.

Mr Lewis nervously escorted her into the downstairs hall, where the hooded caller made some knowing and cryptic remarks about the butler's health, namely the palpitations from which he had recently been suffering, and she offered him a small bottle of hawthorn heart-tonic in return for a silver sixpence. Lewis pocketed the potion and then ushered the gypsy woman into the kitchen, where a young maid named Ann inquired, "Shall I be wetting the tea, Mr Lewis?"

"What on earth are you thinking of, my girl?" interrupted Mrs Hopkins, the cook, shaking her head in disapproval. "You've still got all those pans to scour in the scullery, never mind superstitious nonsense like wetting tea leaves."

But her words fell on deaf ears.

"I'll deal with this, thank you, Mrs Hopkins," said the butler, nodding conspiratorially to Ann.

After settling Mrs Bell down at the big kitchen table, he quickly tiptoed up the stone steps and looked up and down the hall, just in case the master of the house, Mr Williams, had heard or seen the gypsy coming up the drive. The gloomy green-walled hallway was empty and silent, so Lewis returned to the kitchen to find that Mrs Bell had not only pulled her chair up to the fire, but was presently studying young Ann's outstretched palm. She predicted that the young scullery maid would be wooed by a man who worked with a camera in two years' time. Ann blushed and ran off into the scullery, hiding her face in her hands. Another maid, Alice, then entered the kitchen carrying a heavy tray laden with the debris from the afternoon tea in the dining room. Alice was eager to have her palm read as well, but Mrs Bell thundered, "After tea, if you please!"

When the old woman had had her fill of the tea and scones and jam, she made what seemed like a cursory inspection of Alice's palm and pronounced that she was at a major crossroads in her life.

"If you decide to go one way, you will end up sick and forlorn, but if you chose another path, you will come into a great fortune," said Mrs Bell to the open-mouthed maid. "Your destiny lies in your own hands, my dear. Remember that!"

As this mysterious prediction was being digested and discussed, Mr Williams marched into the kitchen and angrily demanded to know what was happening under his roof, but without his permission.

"Mr Lewis! What on earth is going on here? Who let this old crone into the house?"

"I am terribly sorry, sir," said Mr Lewis, bowing his head in shame. He was cringing with embarrassment at having been caught out in front of the other servants. What would this do to his authority in the future? "Er, may I introduce Mrs Bell, sir? She is a gypsy, but one with very impressive powers and I am afraid that it was I who let her into the house."

"I am surprised at you, Lewis. I would have expected better. Throw her out of the house at once. I rely on you to set a good example to the rest of the staff."

The butler, adopting his most subservient posture, sheepishly begged his master's pardon once again. "I am extremely sorry, sir. I don't know what came over me. I suppose I felt sorry for the old woman when she came knocking."

Then, speaking in the old woman's defence, Ann the maid meekly told Mr Williams that Mrs Bell wasn't doing anything wrong and "knew what the stars had in store for a person". Rather than admonishing the girl for her uncharacteristic insolence in answering him back, the master suddenly saw the possibility of a diversion for the ladies and gentlemen upstairs in the drawing room.

"Mm, very well," he said. "I will let it go this time, but if any other vagabonds come knocking, they are not to be allowed into my house without my permission. Do I make myself perfectly clear?"

A chorus of "Yes, sirs" came from the staff.

"Very well then, let that be the end of the matter. Get back to work, all of you. And you, old woman, come with me."

Mrs Williams and her guests were very taken by the idea of having their fortunes told by a genuine gypsy woman and voted that Mr Williams should go first. However, the atmosphere in the room changed dramatically when Mrs Bell told him that he would lose his wife to a man who truly loved her, unless he took pains to rekindle the romance they had once shared. Mrs Williams blushed to the roots of her hair at the prediction and told her husband to send the old woman away, but he shook his head and seemed glassy-eyed, as if the gypsy's prediction had struck a chord deep within his psyche.

The Romany fortune-teller then turned her attention to their two guests, Mr and Mrs Salter. She accurately stated that Mr Salter was a master mariner, but warned that he would lose his life unless he took his wife on a voyage with him "to a distant part of the world". She then delved into her basket and produced a small reel of thread with a gold needle inserted into it.

"This is a healing thread," said the grey-haired oracle, holding out the needle and thread for all to see, "and it will repair any injury. You will need this, my dear. Take it!"

Mrs Salter was a 'sensitive' individual who had a talent for reading people and interpreting dreams, and she offered to pay Mrs Bell for the reel and golden sewing needle, but the old woman refused payment, and simply gave her the thread and left the house.

Everything the gypsy had foretold came to pass. A photographer whom Ann met in Sefton Park during her afternoon off fell deeply in love with her and married her in 1908. The other maid, Alice, becoming discontented with her employers and their strict rules, left the household in search of a new job that summer, and ended up living in a dingy room in a basement. She had only been there a day or two when she remembered Mrs Bell's prophecy. She recognised that the unhealthy damp basement would provide the ideal breeding ground for tuberculosis, so common at that time, and returned to her job as a servant, where at least she would be warm and well fed. This time, her employer lived in a house in Everton, and it was here that she became the best friend and confidant of an old widow. That widow eventually died and left the maid her fortune. Mr Williams did indeed lose his wife, just as the Romany seer had foretold. She ran off with one of his closest friends and went to live in France.

And what about Mrs Bell's strange forecast about the Salters? Well, in the summer of 1906, Captain Salter sailed from Fremantle in Western Australia to Port Natal, nowadays called Durban, in South Africa. He took his wife with him, and when his ship, the *Ancenis* was nearing the South African coast, she ran into a ferocious gale. Three members of the crew were washed overboard during the storm never to be seen again. The heavy seas surged over the decks with seemingly never-ending fury and one particularly violent wave dashed Captain Salter with tremendous force against the ship's rail, splitting his head open.

Mrs Salter had taken the gypsy woman's forecast very seriously and calmly produced the reel and golden needle that she had given her, and then took out a bundle of clean bandages from a first-aid tin. Taking her life in her hands, she tucked up her skirts and waded through the swirling waters and made her way to her seriously injured husband's side. The ship was listing uncontrollably from side to side as the gale roared all around them and, at times, Mrs Salter had to cope with water up to her waist. Yet, in these atrocious conditions, she somehow managed to insert ten stitches into the captain's head wound. This was done with such skill, that the wound was completely healed within a fortnight.

Upon arrival at Port Natal, the captain's injury was examined by a medical man, who was amazed to find that there "were no signs of suppuration" and he complimented Mrs Salter on her highly skilful treatment of a wound that would undoubtedly have led to her husband's death, had it been left untended.

Mrs Salter carried the so-called 'healing thread' with her on further voyages from that time on – just in case.

PINK ELEPHANTS

AND OTHER STRANGE HALLUCINATIONS

Did you know that the man who first spotted the Spanish Armada approaching our shores was a Scouser? He was a ship-owner and captain named Humfraye Brook, and he was sailing from Liverpool to the Canaries, in 1588, when he spotted the advancing Spanish Armada. He calmly turned his ship around and headed straight back to England at full speed. As soon as his ship had weighed anchor, he dispatched messengers bearing the alarming news. Our nation was thus put on alert for the planned Spanish invasion by a Liverpool man. The rest, as they say, is history.

A book as thick as a telephone directory could be written about the Liverpool people who have influenced the world, and even its language. Regular readers of my books and columns will be aware that the phrase 'life of Riley' refers to the truly charmed life of one Mick Riley, born in poverty on Scotland Road in Victorian times, but destined to spend his latter days in the lap of luxury, after marrying a rich American southern belle (see *Strange Liverpool*). Some believe another well-known term, 'Jerry-built' – meaning a badly built dwelling without a firm foundation – originated in Liverpool during the First World War when Germans were nicknamed 'Jerries' – but the jury is still out on that one.

How about the idiom 'seeing pink elephants'? That surreal phrase refers to the hallucinations that seasoned drunks supposedly experience when they withdraw from alcohol. The correct Latin term for this state, and the one used by the medical profession, is Delirium Tremens – the DTs – but there is an old Liverpool story behind the colloquial phrase pink elephants that makes me think it all started right here in Liverpool.

Sunny Jim

In the 1890s, Tommy 'Ringer' Bell, a colourful publican, ran the Bear's Paw public house at Number 62 Irvine Street, Paddington. One evening, around 1893, Bell and a bunch of regulars were discussing the most powerful drinks they had ever tried. The Green Fairy – a concentrated variety of absinthe – was available at the pub, as well as Devil in a Bottle, a ruby rum of shocking proof (190 degrees, or 95 per cent alcohol). Strangled Parrot, available from under the counter, was a legendary spirit of fortified wine that rendered the drinker speechless, but what about Vin Mariani – a wine made with cocaine? Fortunately, Bell did not have a bottle handy.

An old stranger listening to the conversation rapped on the bar to get everyone's attention, and in a beautiful Irish brogue, soliloquised about Bacchus, the Roman god of intoxication. Then, in hushed tones, as if imparting a great secret, he told Bell and the drinkers that he knew the secret of how to mix the most potent drink of all time – Sunny Jim. All the Irishman needed to make this 'euphoric' was five bottles of certain different spirits and a single sunflower – which was quickly procured later that day. The stranger mixed the liquors while everyone looked the other way (as stipulated), and a highly sceptical Tommy Bell volunteered to drink the first glass of Sunny Jim, despite the Irishman's repeated warnings that the drink was capable of inducing hallucinations.

"Oh, come on!" scoffed Tommy. "I'm not in this job for nothing, mister. The drink hasn't been made that can make me see things I don't want to see."

"Okay, That's fine by me, but don't say I didn't warn you."

As all his customers looked on in hushed silence, Tommy took two small sips of the brew, waited a few minutes, and then reported that he was feeling very content with life. He felt no urge to do anything particularly drastic, nevertheless, he did feel compelled, filled as he was with unaccustomed bonhomie, to serve free drinks to all those present. As he handed out the drinks, he could hear the sweet strains of melodious harps, and felt the utmost love towards everyone he looked at. "We are all children," he whispered, smiling with his new found love for his fellow man, when he saw something very unusual looking in through the pub window – the head of an elephant! It had dark human-looking eyes which were full of compassion and wisdom, but the thing which Tommy really couldn't get over, was the colour of the elephant's skin, which was pink and rosy. When the effects of the extraordinary concoction had worn off, people laughed at Bell's vision of the pink elephant. Meanwhile, the Irishman who had mixed the drink had slunk out of the pub unseen with his secret intact. He was never to be seen again.

Could Bell have glimpsed Ganesha, the highly revered elephant-headed Hindu deity, or was it all merely a drug-induced hallucination? Carl Jung, the Swiss psychiatrist, noted that there are familiar recurring figures in world history and literature, which he called archetypes, and perhaps the elephantine apparition witnessed by Bell after drinking Sunny Jim, was merely an archetypal construct of his subconscious.

Was the strange being in the following tale an hallucinatory figment of the imagination, or was it something very real?

The Stick Man

Many years ago a woman wrote to me in desperation after suffering a number of terrifying experiences of a paranormal nature at her home in Liverpool.

It had all started at one o'clock in the morning, in January 1997, when the woman – whom we shall call Amanda – awoke in her bed. Her husband, resting behind her, stroked Amanda's hair affectionately, and this went on for about a quarter of an hour. Then the cordless bedside telephone began to ring and Amanda picked up the receiver. It was her husband. He had rung to say that he was sorry that he hadn't been able to get back home in time, as his car had broken down, but that it was now being repaired.

Amanda froze. If the voice was her husband's – and she was sure it was – who on earth was lying in bed behind her at this moment? Without looking behind, she slowly slid out of bed and walked out of the bedroom. Nevertheless, she caught a glimpse of the stranger, reflected in her dressing table mirror. By the feeble light shining into the room from outside, Amanda could see that her eerie bedfellow was not of this earth and was utterly grotesque.

She shuddered and ran out of the house half-clothed and covered almost half a mile without stopping until she reached the house of a workmate called Sian. When Sian heard her friend's strange tale she tried to convince her that it was just a very vivid nightmare. However, Amanda could not be persuaded to accept this explanation, she knew what she had felt and seen. So Sian agreed to go back with her to check things out. As the two women approached the house they were in time to see Amanda's worried husband standing on the front step. He too tried to make Amanda feel better by saying she'd suffered nothing more than a bad dream, but she would have none of it.

The 'thing' that had stroked Amanda's hair returned on several more occasions, and was seen by other witnesses too. At the back of Amanda's house there is a small wooded area, and on 23 January that same year, two teenaged boys were playing in this wood when one of them went to pick up what he thought was a long bare branch. The 'branch' turned out to have a hand and it snatched at the boy's trainer. The lad screamed and ran off, but his friend clearly saw something long and spindly darting off in the opposite direction. The thing looked vaguely man-shaped but struck him as something alien. The boys returned later with a gang of mates for support, but saw nothing more of the bizarre 'Stick Man', as he came to be nicknamed.

Then, on 22 February, a neighbour of Amanda's called the police after spotting what looked like a burglar climbing over the roof. He looked extremely gangly and long-legged and seemed to be dressed from head to toe in black. He peeped out momentarily from behind Amanda's chimney stack and then vanished. The police were called but found nothing untoward; the house to be safe and secure. They also swept every inch of the roof with their powerful flashlights and established that no one was hiding up there.

Later that night, Amanda's nephew, nine-year-old Matthew, was staying in the spare room in the house, when he was awakened at one o'clock by something clattering and banging on the window pane. He rubbed his eyes, sat up in bed, and gazed out of the window at the full moon, but saw nothing unusual. But as he settled back down into bed, he saw the shadow of a weird, crooked-looking man on the moonlit wall. He turned slowly to get a better look and saw something which triggered a fit, but he was still able to give a good description of the thing when he recovered. An uncanny-looking disjointed man with an abnormally long thorax, and long spindly arms and tapering fingers was pressed up against the window, casting the shadow. His eyes were bright green and glowing, and his fanged mouth was wide open, as if about to bite into something. Radiating from his limbs and head were a series of needle-sharp spines. Matthew came to about twenty minutes later, feeling weak and exhausted.

By the spring of 1997, the sightings of the 'stick man', as he was nicknamed, died down, that is until the evening of Wednesday 30 April, Walpurgis Night (see the chapter in this book entitled The Talisman), a date notorious across the world as the Night of the Dead, when spirits are traditionally able to enter our world with ease. Some occultists also believe it is the date of the Devil's birthday.

On that night, at 11.40pm, Amanda found herself alone at her house once again. Her husband had been forced to stay overnight in Birmingham because of a business meeting, and Amanda's friend Sian had only just left the house after watching television with her for a few hours. Understandably, the supernatural encounters had left Amanda feeling very nervous every time bedtime approached, and going to bed alone was particularly difficult. Knowing she had no choice, she took a deep breath and walked into her bedroom, and was immediately startled by the sight of something in her bed. There was a large bulge under the duvet, and as Amanda looked on, the duvet rose up as if someone beneath it were extending their arms. That was enough! Grabbing her coat, she fled the house in her bare feet and ran to Sian's to tell her about the creepy incident.

This time Sian grabbed her husband's baseball bat and she and Amanda returned to the haunted house. Switching on the light, Sian bravely entered Amanda's bedroom and found that there was indeed someone hiding under the covers. She prodded the bulging duvet with the tip of the baseball bat, which she was holding out at arm's length. Then she lifted the bat, ready to bring it down on the thing under the covers but, in doing so, accidentally smashed the ceiling light – plunging the room into darkness. When the baseball bat struck the duvet, it bounced off the mattress and it was obvious that there was no longer anyone there.

She stumbled out of the room and rushed downstairs to tell Amanda what had happened. Enough was enough, Amanda's nerves were in shreds and she issued her husband with an ultimatum when he got back from his business trip: she would have to leave him unless he agreed to move house. Unfortunately, however, the damage was already done and Amanda's nerves and anxieties got the better of her and she had to be hospitalised in a psychiatric unit for several months before she and her husband could finally move to Widnes.

A year later, the new occupants of the troubled house reported seeing a shadowy figure flitting about the place at night, and a medium of some repute was called in to hold a séance, with the intention of getting in touch with the entity and encouraging it to go elsewhere. However, during the attempt to communicate with the mysterious presence, the medium was violently attacked by an indistinct shadowy figure, and the word 'JAMARAK' was scratched into her back beneath her clothes. Just what exactly who or what

Jamarak was, was never discovered, but fortunately, the entity now seems to have gone into retirement.

The stick man was seen by more than one person, which seems to rule out hallucination, although psychologists maintain that shared hallucinations are entirely possible.

Gargoyle

In a certain church in Liverpool, a couple were rehearsing their forthcoming wedding one afternoon in the 1980s, when they began to argue and harangue each other at the tops of their voices. The young priest was taken aback by the couple's sudden change in attitude: one minute they had appeared to be deeply in love and the next they were fighting like cat and dog, apparently over nothing at all. He sternly reminded them of where they were and why they were there, but the squabbling couple took no notice, and the groom even let loose a four-lettered expletive.

Just then, the priest's attention was caught by something shadowy and unearthly lurking behind one of the stone pillars at the rear of the church. He later said that it could only be described as some kind of gargoyle; a huge hunched figure, apparently made of granite and grotesquely featured with a large mouth that was tusked like a walrus. At that moment, a tremendous peal of thunder shook the church, and large hailstones rained down, pelting the stained-glass windows. An uncanny, unnatural darkness pervaded the church, sweeping over the pews towards the altar with an accompanying iciness.

The sudden storm seemed to be the signal for the demonic creature to spring into action and the priest watched in horror and disbelief, as it loped down the side aisle with its cavernous mouth wide open and its fiery red eyes burning like distress flares. The young cleric suddenly remembered Jesus's bravery as he cast out the Gadarene demons, and so he managed to compose himself and stand his ground, tracing the sign of the cross in the air with his index finger as he willed the fiend to depart. The stone monstrosity was almost upon them, when it stopped in its tracks, and grimaced horribly, and as the fierce crimson lights faded from its eyes, it dissolved into nothingness.

The hailstorm came to an abrupt end, and rays of coloured sunlight filtered prettily through the stained-glass windows once again. The couple ceased arguing so suddenly, that it looked as if a switch had been thrown. They looked first at one another, and then at the priest, with expressions of incomprehension and embarrassment at their uncharacteristic behaviour.

The holy man chose not to reveal what he had witnessed that afternoon, until much later, when he mentioned the scary incident to an older priest, Father Michael, when he was on a visit to another parish. He was surprised, and in a way, relieved, to hear Father Michael say that he too had seen the gargoyle a decade before at the back of the church, when he was officiating at a funeral. At that time, a cleaner in the church had witnessed the same manifestation and had fainted on the spot. The elderly priest was at a loss to explain why and how the entity had managed to infiltrate the church, but firmly believed that it was some mischief-making agent of Satan. He praised his younger colleague for his bravery in facing up to it and thereby rendering it harmless.

Thankfully, the gargoyle has not been seen in the church since.

EVENING IN PARIS

There are two especially powerful things that can trigger a type of mental time travel: songs or music and aromas. How often have you said, "That takes me back" when you have heard a melody from long ago, that has lain cobwebbed in your memory attic for decades; or caught the subtle scent of say, Mansion Polish, that instantly took you back to your childhood days spent in the company of your house-proud grandmother?

Occasionally, we prisoners of the present let go of the 'here and now' and return to the 'then and there', when we enter the realm of sleep, but over the years there have been many cases reported to me in which the mind of a fully conscious person has somehow 'retrograded', or gone back into the past, and these cases reinforce my belief that time is by no means a one-way street, and that 'then' is just as real as 'now'. But the minds of most people, probably out of mundane concerns for such things as mortgages, tax, family ties, relationships, and so on, remain firmly anchored in the present. The past is calling to us all the time, but the buzz and chatter of our thoughts and preoccupations in dealing with the worries of today, swamp it out. However, every now and then, it really is yesterday once more. Here is just one case of what is known as 'retrocognition' which has stuck in my mind.

In 1999, seventy-year-old Jim Wilson had suffered a minor stroke and was recuperating at his sister's home in Huyton. Then, as now, the quality of daytime television was abysmal, and Jim sat there in front of an old television set in a spare room, bored out of his wits. He desperately looked about the room for some kind of diversion and noticed an old trunk in the corner and decided to have a look inside it. It contained old biscuit tins full of outdated insurance policies, yellowed receipts, odd buttons, First Communion cards – and a curious cobalt blue bottle. It was shaped almost like a teardrop, with a gilded pointed top, which Jim automatically began to unscrew. It was an Evening in Paris perfume bottle from the 1930s, used by his long-departed mother. Amazingly, after all that time, the fragrance was not jaded at all, and the seven-year-old Jim, who had been hibernating in the soul of the old man for so long, was instantly awakened and whisked back to 1936.

Jim found himself literally back in the long-lost days of childhood, when his life was still in bud, and before the wicked indoctrination by those children who had gone to seed – adults – had had its effect. The spare room's walls fell away and the din from the television was replaced by the exquisite sound of birdsong. Jim looked around him to see a carpet of bobbing bluebells and leafy green arches in a familiar wood. Dragons, knights and fabulous creatures of the imagination roamed those woods in Huyton, and now Jim was running through the forest with his little magpie-coated dog Stan rushing on ahead.

Then, without warning, Jim was suddenly thrust back into that dreary room again, in 1999, with his sister tugging at his elbow. Struggling to find the right words, he told her what had happened but she just ushered him over to an armchair and advised him to get some rest. He closed his fist around the tiny blue scent bottle, as he sensed that its sweet-smelling magic had somehow jogged an amazingly tactile memory; a memory that he was desperate to recapture. He told his sister that she was right, he wanted to have his usual little siesta, and so she left him to have a two-hour snooze, saying it was the best thing for him, but Jim had no intentions of going to sleep.

He relaxed back into the easy chair, lifted the neck of the blue bottle to his nostrils and sampled once again the delights of recapturing his yesteryears. He was instantly transported back to a better time and place. This time he was walking up Huyton's old Baker Street, hand-in-hand with Eleanor, his first love, whom he had forgotten all about! She was looking skyward to an airship passing by, high in the clouds.

"Eleanor, will you marry me?" Jim suddenly found himself blurting out to her.

"What did you say?" asked Eleanor, dreamily, as she turned her green eyes away from the dirigible to Jim, and he repeated the question. "But we're only children, Jim," she laughed, and then added, "But okay, yes, I will."

The two youngsters stood amidst the tranquil hush of the graveyard of St Michael's Church, with bees lazily droning around them in the still summer air. Beneath the children's feet, coffined in the clay, outside of space and time, slept hundreds of lost Victorian souls, and Jim drowsily spelt out one of their graven names from a mossy headstone. "Peter Beesley, who met his death by … What's that word, Ellie?"

"Accident," said Eleanor and then read out the rest of the inscription. "He died in 1884, aged seventeen. That's so sad, isn't it?"

But Eleanor's seven-year-old brain soon forgot Peter Beesley's untimely demise, as she gracefully plucked a dandelion which had gone to seed and blew its wispy parachutes into the blue Saturday afternoon sky. She then discussed with Jim their plans of marriage, and pointed out that they were in need of a priest to marry them; it couldn't be done without one. Jim suggested Harry Shilottle, the son of a local Irish priest. Shilottle was duly accosted by the young couple at the sweetshop on Tarbock Road, and was bribed into acting as priest for the forthcoming marriage ceremony by the offer of half a tuppeny bar of Fry's Chocolate Cream.

The deal was done and the three children gathered at the back of St Michael's Church on the following Sunday morning. Harry Shilottle held a small black Bible belonging to his father, across his chest, merely as a prop, as he intoned, "In the presence of God, Father, Son and Holy Spirit, we have come together to witness the marriage of Jim and Eleanor, to pray for God's blessing on them, to share their joy and to celebrate their love."

After a promising start, Harry then struggled to remember some of the other parts of the wedding service, but managed to recall, "Do you,

Eleanor, take Jim as your lawfully wedded husband?"

"I do," replied Eleanor, smiling broadly.

"And do you, Jim, take Eleanor as your wife?"

"Yes, I do!" said Jim eagerly.

"Okay, I now pronounce you man and wife ... and er ... may the Lord have mercy on your souls!" said Harry, unsure of the closing words to the ceremony.

Jim and Eleanor kissed, and Harry took handfuls of rice from his pockets and showered the 'newly-weds'.

They were just discussing what to do next, when a stern voice thundered out, "What on earth are you three doing?' and interrupted the romantic fun.

The children viewed the approaching vicar with alarm. Eleanor dropped her posie of wild flowers and Harry Shilottle dropped his father's Bible and scarpered. When the priest saw the rice on the ground, the discarded Bible and the two seven-year-olds clutching hands, he put two and two together, and told them not to be so silly. Marriage was a holy sacrament and was only for grown-ups. Eleanor protested that they weren't being silly, and that she loved Jim, and he loved her. The children ran away from the vicar and decided they would find some empty house in which to live together; a rather ambitious plan for two children not yet out of infant school!

By the early evening, their worried parents collared them wandering aimlessly about on Derby Road and took them back to their separate homes.

Not long afterwards, Eleanor and her family moved away from the area and Jim never saw his childhood sweetheart again ...

... Jim Wilson sighed and found himself once again sitting in the armchair at his sister's house – now aged seventy again, and clutching the magical blue perfume bottle, which was now empty. The Evening in Paris aroma had completely evaporated during his long 'reverie'. He held the slim neck of the elegant bottle to his nostrils once again, desperate to recapture the precious memories it had provoked, but only the weakest trace of the scent remained. The door to the past had been firmly relocked. Tears welled up in the old man's eyes, as he made an important resolution; he had to find Eleanor again. He knew the impulse was crazy after a gap of sixty-three years, but his trip into the past had opened up his heart and put him back in touch with his emotions. He had never known a yearning like this before. It was so powerful that it couldn't be ignored.

Jim's nephew was sympathetic and offered to help him in his quest. He searched the internet for Eleanor and finally managed to trace her because of her unusual surname. She was alive and well and was now living in Cheshire.

Emails were exchanged between the childhood sweethearts and eventually Jim and Eleanor met at the Adelphi Hotel in Liverpool. She had vivid memories of the 'wedding' and she told Jim that she had been married twice since those days, but was now a widow. The couple got on famously and began to go out on dates together and eventually married just six months later. Jim's physical condition gradually improved, and a year later he had made a full recovery from the stroke.

The couple are still going strong today, and Jim still has that blue perfume bottle which acted as a powerful memory evoker – or did that scent really transport him back to his first and last love?

OF UNSOUND MIND

The Masked Intruder

One afternoon in April 1967, thirty-five-year-old Marianne Hill entered her Dovecot home laden with carrier bags after a trip to the shops. She unpacked the shopping and put it all away and then went upstairs to get something from her bedroom, little suspecting that she was in for the shock of her life. For there, hanging from the light fitting, was the body of an eerily familiar woman. In fact, that woman looked exactly like herself and was even wearing her clothes. Mrs Hill shot out of the bedroom, down the stairs and out into the street, quite unable to scream.

An off-duty postman came upon his distressed neighbour wandering in the road, occasionally gazing up at her bedroom window with an expression of utter terror.

"Hey! What's the matter, love?" he asked. "You look like you've had a bit of a fright."

"In my bedroom ... woman ... hanging ... she's in my bedroom ... hanging" said the distraught woman, incoherently, pointing to her upstairs window.

"What's in your bedroom, Mrs Hill," coaxed the postman, gently. "Come on now, you can tell me all about it."

"It's her ... she's hanging from the light ... and she looks ... she looks ... just like me!"

After Mrs Hill had finally managed to stammer out this somewhat unintelligible reply, the postman gently shepherded her into his own house, and then ran to the nearest telephone box to alert the police and summon an ambulance – just in case the hanged woman – if indeed there was one – was still alive.

Having left his wife looking after Mrs Hill, the postman then went across to her home and upstairs into the bedroom, where his neighbour's 'look-alike' was supposedly to be found hanging. He braced himself against what he thought he might encounter. But there was no corpse dangling from the light, or anywhere else for that matter, yet he did come across something very bizarre and equally creepy. Hanging by a flex noose from the light fitting was a mannequin of some kind. It had on a wig that mimicked the exact same hairstyle and hair colouring as Marianne Hill, and the clothes which the dummy wore had been removed from her wardrobe – right down to the underwear and footwear.

The police turned up and because they couldn't find any evidence of a break-in, or even a crime, as such, they dismissed the whole thing as a rather distasteful practical joke, presumably perpetrated by someone with whom Mrs Hill had had an argument. It was April after all, commented the postman, who also concluded that the whole thing must have been some late April fool stunt.

When Mrs Hill was sufficiently recovered, she was persuaded to return to the house, accompanied by the postman and his wife for moral support. They went up to the bedroom with her and there she studied the mannequin's face. Whoever had put the mannequin there had gone to a lot of trouble to make it look authentic. They had not only stuck a pair of her false eyelashes on it, but had even carefully coated the dummy's lips with Marianne's own lipstick.

Not surprisingly, Marianne was very badly shaken by the hanging dummy incident, and slept on the sofa that night, leaving the lights on in the hall, living room and kitchen. Throughout the night she had the pricklish sensation of being watched by someone, and she kept the curtains and blinds drawn until well after sunrise, but otherwise, the night was uneventful.

Three days later, an electricity man called at 2 o'clock in the afternoon and told Marianne that he had come to change her meter under the stairs. She was glad of the company, as she was still feeling shaky and she offered the electrician a cup of tea. He politely declined, then asked her if she had left any electrical appliances on all night, as he scrutinised the dials of the electric meter. She nodded and admitted that she had left the lights on in the hallway, kitchen and living room throughout the last three nights.

"What for?" asked the electricity man. "D'you always do that? It must cost you a fortune when you get your 'leccy bill.'"

"No, I usually switch all the lights off when I go to bed, but something terrible happened the other day and now I'm afraid of the dark. I know it's silly."

Mrs Hill went on to describe the shock of finding the mannequin hanging in her bedroom, and the electricity man, a small square-shouldered individual, with shoulder-length raven hair and a thick black 'gunslinger' moustache, was rather unsympathetic and couldn't help but grin when she mentioned the underwear. She was cross at first, but then realised that it must have sounded comical to him.

"Yeah, I suppose that would have given me the creeps as well," he said, suppressing a smirk as he checked the fuse-box.

"Do you think it's been somebody's idea of a joke?" asked Marianne rather tetchily.

Despite being rather annoyed that he seemed to think the whole business funny, she found herself being strangely attracted to the electricity man, which surprised her, as she usually went for much taller men.

"Probably," the electrician replied, whilst opening a small canvas tool bag. He rummaged around in it for a while and then said, "Do me a favour, will you, love?"

"Yeah, sure, what?" said Marianne squinting into the dark cubby hole under the stairs.

"Can you go into the kitchen and make sure nothing's plugged in, and wait there till I shout you?"

"Yeah, sure."

Marianne Hill went off straight away and checked each of the electrical gadgets. She had to pull out one or two of the appliances to get at the plugs and the last thing to be unplugged was the electric toaster. She had been in the kitchen less than three minutes in all when she returned to the hallway, even though she hadn't heard the electrician call her – but he was nowhere to be seen. She went into the living room and looked out of the window, perhaps hoping to see him fetching his tools, or the replacement meter from his van. But there was no van outside and no electrician.

"I've turned everything off in the kitchen, like you said," she shouted, but there was no reply. She opened the front door, stepped outside, and looked both ways. He was still nowhere to be seen.

Marianne went back into her house, utterly perplexed, and went to look round upstairs. Perhaps he'd gone the toilet? No, the toilet was empty. She opened her bedroom door and gasped. There, on the bed, someone had carefully laid out her navy skirt and matching jacket, with a pair of her stockings positioned so that hey led from the skirt to a pair of shoes. The handle of what was subsequently identified as a long chef's knife, protruded from the bed. The blade had been driven through the front of the navy jacket and into the bedding. On the floor lay a collapsed hollow 'face'; the rubber mask, with a fine head of black hair attached and a moustache, had obviously been discarded by the so-called electrician. On the dressing table mirror, scrawled in lipstick in capital letters were the words: 'They put me away because of you!'

Dizzy with fear, Marianne Hill backed out of her room, expecting the unbalanced impostor to come chasing after her. Steadying herself on the banister she descended the stairs and groped her way with difficulty to the front door. She tried to open it, but it had been bolted at the bottom. Then she heard the sly chuckling behind her and felt the sweaty hand grabbing at her hair. She screamed, bent down, and somehow managed to slide the bolt sideways and yank open the door. As she did so, the eerie voice behind her cried, "Now! Now!"

Mrs Hill shot out of the house like a cork from a bottle, with just one thing on her mind – escape. She was oblivious to everything around her and was almost run down by a passing motorcyclist who had to swerve to avoid her. Passersby went to her aid and the police arrived at the house within fifteen minutes. Who could blame them for being sceptical about the story? Three days ago they had been called out to a suspected suicide, which turned out to be nothing more than a dangling mannequin. The knife in the mattress of Marianne's bed was dusted for fingerprints, but none were found. These days, the knife and discarded rubber mask would no doubt have provided the police with DNA samples, but in those days no such technology existed and anyway, it was all deemed to be an attention-seeking hoax, unworthy of serious investigation.

But that is not the end of the story. Mrs Hill left Dovecot and moved to St Helens, where she stayed with her ex-husband for a while before moving to the Dingle. She wrote to me at Radio Merseyside to try and make some sense of her experiences, and I must admit that I did not know what to make of it, and it stayed on my file, metaphorically gathering dust, as one of the many unsolved mysteries which come my way. However, three years afterwards, my interest in Marianne's story was revived when fifty-five-year-old Sheila emailed me with an another intriguing story ...

Three Sheets to the Wind

In April, 1987, a little old lady knocked on the door of Sheila's Dovecot home one evening. She seemed confused and asked Sheila – who lived alone – if she could use her toilet. The old woman said she had been looking for an old friend's house and had lost her bearings – and apparently her memory. All she could remember was that her house was in a road in Huyton near Woolfall Heath. Sheila told her that she would phone her son and he would drive her home. She put the kettle on after waiting outside the toilet door for the old woman to come out.

"I'm just washing my hands," the old lady called from the other side of the toilet door. "I had a fall you see, dear."

As the kettle was beginning to boil, Sheila hurried up the stairs again and knocked on the toilet door, but got no answer. Fearing that the elderly visitor had collapsed, she tried the door, and it opened. The toilet was empty but the hot water tap was running in the wash basin. Sheila began to get suspicious about the old lady, and wondered if she was only pretending to be confused, when in fact she was actually a thief in disguise. So, Sheila crept on tiptoe towards her bedroom door. She turned the handle, trying not to make a sound. As the door opened a small white feather drifted on to her face. The Dovecot widow looked in dismay at the state of her room. The pillows had been ripped open, and the feathers were drifting down like a small blizzard – suggesting that this frenzied act was very, very recent! In the middle of the bed, a long carving knife had been plunged into the mattress.

What was going on? Where had the old woman disappeared to? Then Sheila noticed something out of the corner of her eye – lying on the floor was a crumpled head and neck, with stringy grey hair attached. Sheila recoiled but soon realised that the 'head' was actually a thin latex mask of an wrinkled old woman's visage, with a wig of grey hair attached, partially tied up in a small bun.

Something else troubled her. There was something missing from the room. A sickening thought suddenly crossed Sheila's mind. Her old cat Fifi was nowhere to be seen, yet she invariably slept curled up on her bed in the evenings. The fear she felt was so intense it was physical, and yet she was also furious at having been duped and her beloved pet threatened. Picking up a heavy metal framed picture of her late husband, she prepared herself to strike out at this weirdo who had invaded her house and taken advantage of her by pretending to be an old woman.

Steeling herself against what she might find inside, Sheila flung open her wardrobe doors, but there was nothing there except her clothes and shoes and a couple of handbags. Then she gingerly lifted the bedcovers and looked underneath the bed, dreading finding the creepy intruder. Instead, she found Fifi, cowering behind some old suitcases; the only other witness to the horrors of that evening.

Sheila cradled the cat in her arms and smothered her with kisses. She carried her downstairs, and then took her across the road to her friend's. The police were called out, but they couldn't find the intruder, despite going through the house with a fine-toothed comb. Sheila could not get her head round the way the impersonator had managed to get out of the house without passing her. He or she had definitely not escaped via the upstairs bedroom window, because it was still locked from the inside, and no one had been heard coming down the stairs.

About six months later, Sheila's son had to go into hospital for a minor operation, and one evening after visiting him, she boarded the bus, as usual, back to Huyton. Sitting on a seat facing her was an old man and there was something vaguely familiar about him. Sheila racked her brains but couldn't place him, but judging by the way he was looking at her, he certainly remembered her from somewhere. The old man suddenly got up, and she saw that he was very small for a man, and he disembarked at the next stop.

As the bus drove on, Sheila felt butterflies in her stomach, because it suddenly came to her where she had seen that man – he had undoubtedly been the person who had worn that thin latex mask that evening in April, whilst pretending to be a distraught old woman. His eyes had been the dead give away, together with his small build. When Sheila reached her stop, she hurried home, looking behind her every few seconds, in case the old oddball had followed her, and she sat up most of the night with the doors bolted and the windows securely locked. However, that night her fears proved groundless.

Indeed, she saw no more of the sinister female impersonator, but in the following year, on 14 February, she received a Valentine's Day card from someone who signed himself as, 'You know who (three sheets to the wind) xxx'.

'Three sheets to the wind' is an old expression, originally meaning 'very drunk' but in Liverpool the phrase is usually used to denote lunacy, and Sheila believes that the strange old man she saw on the bus that night was definitely of unsound mind.

Sheila has since moved to Crosby, and as far as I know, there have been no further strange intrusions into her former house in Huyton.

So what is the connection between Marianne's and Sheila's stories? I hear you asking. You have probably already guessed. Yes, that house is the very same one where Marianne Hill lived twenty years before Sheila. Their experiences, taken together, make a very unusual case, but someone out there with knowledge of that building can probably throw some light upon it.

STRANGE CREATURES OF THE SUBURBS

On the Run

Terry, a reader from Whiston, is today a respectable businessman nearing retirement, but back in 1962, he was a small-time seventeen-year-old thief and tearaway, on the run from Borstal. For younger readers, may I explain that Borstal was a strict juvenile detention centre, designed to reform 'hard-knock' serial male offenders between the ages of seventeen and twenty-one. The harsh regime was highly disciplined, and the severity of the punishment usually guaranteed that most inmates feared a return visit to the place, although many inevitably did. Borstal was abolished in 1982 –

although many people believed its abolition was a big mistake, as it did provide an effective deterrent against youth crime.

Anyway, back to the story.

In October 1962, Terry escaped from a Lancashire Borstal and went on the run, covering over ten miles on foot to reach his home in Huyton. But, of course, the police were on the lookout for him there, so he borrowed a tent from a friend and, camouflaging it with bits of foliage, he camped out in a field near Childwall Valley Road, close to the railway embankment. His friends Roy, Billy and Paddy, all aged sixteen, regularly visited his secret hideaway, bringing him food, drink and the odd cigarette. They even supplied him with a portable 'Murphy' transistor radio, stolen from an allotment hut. Terry regaled his friends with his exciting plan to start a new life as a jazz musician in New York under an alias. When the "heat died down", movie-influenced Terry said he would board a liner and cross the Atlantic. The reality was to prove a little different!

During his second night in the tent, a bone-chilling October fog enveloped the whole of Childwall, and Terry shuddered under his thin canvas roof, as he suddenly became aware of some weird pipe music. Remembering that he was supposed to be a toughnut, he undid the tent flap and peeped out. He could see nothing but a ghostly full moon just managing to penetrate the thick nocturnal vapours. He crept back into the tent but did not get a wink of sleep for the rest of the night.

On the following night, Terry bullied Billy and Paddy into staying with him in the tent, saying it was a real laugh – they'd love it. Of course, secretly he was too afraid of spending another night on his own in the secluded field. The three lads sat in the tent laughing and joking till the early hours, and this time there was no fog outside. Other than themselves, there was no sound except the owls hooting in the distant trees, and the odd rumble of a train trundling down the tracks to Hunts Cross, to break the silence of the night. That was until about an hour after midnight, when the lads were finally trying to settle down and get some sleep. They would be quiet for a few minutes, then one of them would say something funny and the giggles would break out again. But the three of them instantly stopped larking about and sat bolt upright when the strange pipe music came floating in the air once again.

"It's coming from right over that way, somewhere up by Jackson's Pond," Paddy, reckoned.

"Ssh! Be quiet!" Terry whispered.

Billy, showing off in front of his mates that he was braver than them, opened the tent flap and poked his head out. What he saw would send him haring all the way back to his home in Hartsbourne Avenue without pausing for breath. A strange mythical creature was stepping gracefully across the field in the moonlight. It looked just like Pan, the old God of music and mischief, that the lads had come across in their reading books in primary school. It had curved horns like a ram, hairy cloven-hoofed limbs from the knees down, and it was playing a set of reed flutes. Billy was not going to wait to be introduced and, without telling the others what he had seen, he gulped down a scream, and ran off as fast as his legs would carry him.

Paddy reacted in exactly the same way when he saw the sinister creature, but he was less fortunate in that it chased after him, screaming with manic laughter. It pursued him as far as the hedge at the far side of the field, where it came to a halt, but Paddy ran non stop until he reached his home on Chelwood Avenue, close to Childwall Valley High School.

Terry, meanwhile, was still cringing in the tent doorway, desperately trying to think up an escape plan. As Paddy disappeared from view over the hedge, he watched, horrified, as the horned monster turned around and headed back in his direction. He shot out of the tent and ran to Barnham Drive, where he was collared by a policeman walking his night beat. In normal circumstances, an encounter with the law would have been the last thing Terry wanted, but on this night the policeman was definitely the lesser of the two evils, and an almost welcome sight. However, Terry's Pan story only elicited sarcasm, "Been on the purple hearts, have you, lad?" smirked the bobby. His brief period of captivity was over, but Terry was actually relieved, because the thought of spending another night in that spooky field made him break out in a cold sweat.

Some months later, the frightening faun-like creature was allegedly seen in the area again, this time on the eve of the notorious Childwall Valley Road Murder, in which twelve-year-old schoolgirl Lesley Hobbs was brutally killed. On this occasion, three perfectly sane adults returning home up Origen Road at 11 o'clock at night, saw the cloven-footed figure meandering about in the middle of the Boys' Club Playing Field. The witnesses watched in disbelief as the horned man, having caught sight of them and taken fright, trotted away across the fields and was lost in the darkness.

Winged Menace

Another improbable creature was sighted in Liverpool's suburbs by a retired joiner Peter, who was a pupil at St Christopher's School in Speke when he was eleven, back in 1963. One weekend in that year, he was staying with his aunt at her prefab home on Sandgate Road, when an incident took place which has haunted him ever since. Peter remembers the date clearly, because it was same the day that President Kennedy was assassinated – Friday 22 November 1963.

At around 7.45pm on that memorable date, Peter was playing with three friends outside his aunt's home, when all four children heard an unusual screeching sound – coming from high above them. Four faces turned skywards, and in the moonlight, the kids saw a man with bat-like wings making a slow descent. This improbable figure landed with a gentle thud, quite close to them, too close for comfort, in fact! It swivelled round to face the awe-struck children, whose fascination quickly turned to horror when they saw that the strange being had horns like the devil and had a malignant air of evil about it. The sight sent them scattering in different directions to their various homes.

When Peter told his aunt what he had seen she assumed he was telling fibs, but when he said, "Okay, look out the window then and you'll see him yourself," she too saw the weird winged humanoid. As they watched, it began to flap its gigantic wings, which soon lifted it off the ground and back up into the sky.

The same menacing entity returned to the area a week later on the night of a full moon, and this time it was witnessed by many people, including a policeman, as it flew towards the Metal Box factory. This same inexplicable airborne being was apparently seen over a wider area throughout the summer of 1969, in places ranging from Speke to Hunt's Cross, Halewood, Huyton and Knowsley. Coincidentally, throughout the same time period, there were also reports of a flying black woman seen in the skies over Da Nang in South Vietnam. It was not only the locals that saw the woman; several US marines on guard duty also testified to having seen her. Witnesses described her as having bat-like wings about ten feet in diameter.

Years before, in the early 1960s, a bizarre-looking winged figure nicknamed 'Mothman' was seen by dozens of people in the state of West Virginia, and, like its counterparts in Da Nang and Liverpool, it was never satisfactorily explained, but largely dismissed as the product of mass hysteria.

Devil Dog

A round the mid-1960s, an even more frightening creature made its presence felt in northern Liverpool: a demonic black dog of mind-blowing proportions. Sightings of this jet-black monster canine have been reported to me many times over the years, but one of the closest encounters with this 'devil dog' took place one night in the middle of an old tenement building, Chaucer House, off Scotland Road.

A gang of six boys, aged around ten, had hatched a plot to stay out all night without their parents' permission. Sneaking out of their various flats after everyone had gone to sleep clutching blankets and food that they had filched from their mums' kitchens, the lads rendezvoused as planned and started setting up camp in the square in the middle of the tenement. Because of the cold weather, one of the lads had built a small fire and they all huddled round it, revelling in their new-found freedom and tucking into the odd assortment of pilfered food.

Just after midnight, a black dog the size of a Great Dane loped into the square, probably attracted by the flames. The boys all later described the monster dog as having eyes like hot coals and a wicked, human-like face. They didn't hang around to see what the dog would do next, but even in their haste to get away from the loathsome thing, several of them saw a man in a wide black sombrero hat and a long cloak striding into the square after the dog. He had metal studs on the heels of his boots, making his footsteps echo throughtout the square. He laughed demonically, then shouted mockingly, "Come back, children, my dog won't harm you, will you, Shuck?"

Despite this assurance, the devilish-looking stranger and his hound of the Baskervilles look-alike immediately gave chase. Its fanged teeth bared, the slavering hound snapped at the children's heels and they only just made it home to their respective flats in the nick of time.

A local priest was brought in to warn the children about the dangers of staying out after dark and making fires, not to mention worrying their parents half to death. He instilled fear into the boys by telling them that they had been chased by none other than the Devil himself and his murderous Hell Hound 'Shuck'. Even without the priest's lecture, the boys had had a salutary lesson, which dampened their spirit of adventure for many years to come.

Chaucer House tenements have long since been demolished, but the spooky memories of the Devil and his Hell Hound live on in the minds of those six people who came across them on that wintry night.

TIMESLIPS

As you read this, both you, and the earth upon which you stand, are travelling at a speed of eighteen miles per second around the sun, and simultaneously, the sun and its family of planets are also orbiting the galaxy at one hundred and thirty-five miles per second. Should you live to an average age of seventy-five years, you will have travelled a staggering 320,191,479,975 miles across the universe in a complex corkscrew trajectory. That is an awful lot of space travelled, but how about travelling in time? Is such a thing possible, or is it just the stuff of science fiction writers?

In May 2008, the controversial Large Hadron Collider, or LHC – a gigantic particle accelerator – began its operations in the suburbs of Geneva, in Switzerland. Many scientists are convinced that this incredible machine will be powerful enough to create mini black holes and 'wormholes' – shortcuts through space and time. The intelligence services of the world will be carefully monitoring the LHC, in case some terrorist or dictator from the future should attempt to send information back in time to 2008, with the intention of changing history to suit themselves. This information could cause mind-bending paradoxical loops, or simply alter world affairs as they unfold, by revealing important future events (such as the exact time and date when some dictator, with nuclear weapons at his disposal, should decide to start World War III, for example).

So much for theoretical timewarps, but how about the ones that have already been documented? The stories which follow are just two examples of the many hundreds of timeslip incidents that I have collected over the years.

Waylaid in Winwick

In 1977, Liverpool coach driver Frank Matthews was hired to take a group of people from Warrington to Blackpool for the day. After a fun day out sampling the delights of the resort, the weary passengers climbed back into the charabanc and left Blackpool at around 8pm for the return fifty-mile return journey. Because of motorway delays, the coach was late in returning, and as it was passing through the Newton-le-Willows area, something inexplicable took place. A dark misty object flew alongside the coach, parallel to the ground, startling the thirty-plus passengers from their torpor. This nebulous anomaly began ramming itself against the windows and sides of the vehicle, shaking the coach each time it did so, before vanishing from view. Shortly afterwards the benighted coach ran into thick a fog – and the macadamised highway quickly tapered off into a narrow dirt track. The driver had completely lost his bearings and the coach rocked about on the uneven grassy ground, jolting the passengers who looked at each other in disbelief. This really was becoming the journey from Hell.

By this time the coach should have been nearing Winwick, but there were no buildings to be seen anywhere and as the confused driver agonised over how to extricate himself from the situation, three men on horseback galloped up to the coach. These horsemen wore metal breastplates and distinctive 'lobster pot' cavalry helmets – of the type worn by Oliver Cromwell's seventeenth century troops. The outdated trio circled round the coach. The driver, Matthews, realising that something was gravely amiss, locked the door of the charabanc, restarted the engine, slammed it into reverse gear and backed rapidly over the lumpy terrain.

The coach headlights blazed, their strong beams crazily cutting through the fog and startling two of the horses. Matthews repeatedly sounded the coach's horn in an attempt to scare them off. But the effect was only temporary; the three horses would rear up and back away for a short distance, but would soon return as their curious expert riders brought them back under control. Eventually, the fog began to lift and the wide road reappeared. At the same time, the three soldiers slowly dissolved into the air as the familiar grim outline of Winwick Hospital loomed into view.

A Civil War battle took place in the area of this timeslip in 1649, and for some unknown reason, it would seem that time often flips backwards to the days of the Roundheads and Cavaliers, in the area between Newton-le-Willows and Winwick. In 1949, for example, a vehicle carrying a group of Widnes rugby supporters suffered a puncture near Winwick. As they waited for the wheel to be changed, the supporters were entertained for a full thirty minutes by three Cromwellian soldiers trotting about over some fields in the distance. They were still visible even as the coach drove off after the repair had been completed.

A Tanner from a Copper

S ome timeslips are so mundane that a witness may not even realise that he has been into the past at all, until some vital piece of information comes to light.

In the late 1960s, a woman named Eleanor was shopping in Woolton Village with her son Stan, when he accidentally cut his hand. Eleanor panicked, because the cut was quite deep and probably needed a few stitches. She bandaged the hand with a clean handkerchief as best she could and then hurried to the bus stop, where she waited anxiously for the next bus, hoping that it would take them to the nearest hospital.

However, when Eleanor searched in her bag for some change for the fare, she discovered that she had lost her purse. By this time, Stan's hand had started to throb painfully and the bandage was almost completely soaked through with blood. So she bustled him to Woolton Police Station, where she told the desk sergeant about her predicament. Within seconds, the cheerful old policeman had produced a 'tanner' from his pocket and gave it to Eleanor.

"Oh, that's really kind of you, sir. Thank you very much," said Eleanor. "And I promise to pay you back as soon as I can." Then turning to her son she said, "Say thank you to the kind policeman, Stan."

"No hurry, my dear. You just make sure your young 'un's alright," said the desk sergeant, with a kindly smile, and he directed her to the nearest hospital with an A and E department.

True to her word, Eleanor returned sometime later and told a young constable behind the desk that she would like to return a tanner to the older sergeant who had helped her out the other day. The young policeman was baffled, because he had been the only person on desk duty during the day for the past few months. Then a sergeant came out from the back room and asked what the matter was. When Eleanor told him, the sergeant asked where this older policeman had come from.

Eleanor pointed to a specific door behind the counter on the left-hand side. The sergeant opened that door to reveal a derelict room, full of broken bits of discarded furniture. Apparently, the station was due to close down in the near future, and that room had been out of use for quite some time.

Eleanor did not know what to make of it all and was just about to leave, when she noticed a framed photograph on the wall of the sergeant who had loaned her the sixpence, and she pointed to the picture, saying, "That's him there!" The sergeant smiled and said that the sergeant in the photograph was probably dead by now, as that picture dated back to the 1930s and none of the present staff had ever worked with the policeman in the picture, although they were all aware that he had been a very well respected member of the force. Eleanor shuddered upon hearing this and could only conclude that either a sympathetic ghost had lent her the very solid sixpence, or she had somehow stepped back into the Woolton of bygone days.

The mystery of this timeslip was never solved.

A Macabre Duet

One of the many mistakes made in the awful *Diary of Jack the Ripper* – a book that is alleged to have been written by the infamous Whitechapel Murderer himself – is the line, 'I took refreshment at the Poste House'. In 1888, the Poste House pub (situated at Number 23 Cumberland Street, off Dale Street) was, in fact, called the New Post Office, and was run by a publican by the name of George Barratt. It was not renamed as the Poste House until many years after the death of Ripper suspect, James Maybrick, so how on earth could he have known its future name?

Anyway, although Jack the Ripper never took refreshment in the Poste House, the premises have played host to many strange goings-on over the years, and has been frequented by such eminent personages as Prince Louis Napoleon, who later became the French Emperor, as well as a motley selection of low-life scoundrels such as Jack Garratt – a Tranmere man notorious for trying to sell his wife for ten guineas to a sea captain; and also for conman Davy Roberts, a swindler from Nantymoel in South Wales, who maintained that he was the Uncrowned Ruler of Ireland, directly descended from King Cormac Longbeard.

Around the year 1895, on the night of Halloween, the landlord of the New Post Office was awaiting the arrival of two old friends, Mickey and Johnno, who were due to visit him from Manchester. Both men were in their twenties and possessed great musical talent, and whenever they visited their friend's drinking establishment, on Cumberland Street, they would perform a magnificent duet on the pub's upright piano, playing a medley of classical music and popular songs to the delight of the other drinkers.

However, Mickey and Johnno failed to arrive at the pub on Halloween, and it was thought the lads must have had business to attend to and would turn up a day or so later than usual. After washing all the glasses and generally putting the pub straight, the landlord and his wife eventually went off to bed at around 1 o'clock. Some time later, when they were both sound asleep, they were startled awake by the sound of a piano playing somewhere in the building.

The landlord pulled on his dressing gown and lit a candle. He and his wife looked at each other as they tried to decide where the music was coming from. Surely it couldn't be their piano? But they soon realised that it was indeed coming from their piano downstairs. Assuming that drunken burglars were responsible, and against his wife's wishes, he fetched his loaded pistol from the dresser drawer and crept downstairs to investigate.

When he was halfway down the stairs, the alehouse-keeper stopped and listened again to the other-worldly tune that was being hammered out on his piano, and although he didn't recognise it at once, it was definitely being played in the inimitable four-hands style of Mickey and Johnno. Had his two overdue friends from Manchester gained entry to the pub, perhaps by climbing through a window, rather than wake them up? If so, it was very uncharacteristic of them.

The landlord shook his head good-naturedly and smiled to himself as he opened the door a fraction – but despite the continuing music, he found the bar in total darkness. He inched his way across the uneven floor and lifted his candle to behold a grisly sight; two complete human skeletons were sitting side by side at the piano, and their bony fingers were moving nimbly up and down the keyboard in unison. The skull of one of the players turned to face the shocked landlord and its jaw opened and closed with a horrible clacking sound for a few heart-stopping moments, as it mimicked his laughter, the laughter, which, by this time, had dried up altogether.

The publican clutched the edge of the bar to steady himself, as he felt the blood draining from his head and his legs beginning to give way beneath him. The song which the skeletal pianists were playing was now clearly recognisable to him as Chopin's Funeral March, although they were playing it with much more gusto than the solemn and reverential piece demanded. He futiley fired his pistol at one of the skeletons, more or less as a reflex action, and then scrabbled his way back upstairs, where he barricaded himself and his wife into their bedroom until dawn.

The next day, the publican learned the sad news that Mickey and Johnno had died some weeks previously. Mickey had died shortly after contracting a typhoid-like fever and then, just days later, Johnno had fallen down the stairs whilst drunk and broken his neck. The landlord immediately thought back to that night and the skeletons, and didn't know whether to laugh or cry.

Beware The Knife Woman
of Roscoe Street

As readers of my books will be aware, ghosts can appear at any time and in any place, but encounters with these enigmatic entities for some reason seem to occur more frequently during the winter months of December and January and the following incident is a case in point.

At 6am on 27 December 1962, twenty-one-year-old Stuart decided to take a short-cut down Roscoe Street in Liverpool city centre. He had just left an all-night party on Duke Street, and instead of walking back to his home in Kensington, he had decided to call on his ex-girlfriend Nancy, at her bed-sit on Clarence Street. Heavy snow was falling, and the deep frozen blanket of snow that had already fallen, in one of the coldest winters on record, crunched under Stuart's boots. He fastened the topmost button of his jacket, pulled up his collar and thrust his gloveless hands under his armpits for warmth, as he made his way up the poorly-lit street, half blinded by the stinging cold flakes which were coming at him horizontally.

Suddenly, he made out a figure standing upright in the distance. The figure seemed to be that of a woman and she was standing stock still in the centre of the road, close to the Mount Pleasant junction. Stuart was slightly intoxicated from his night out, but still felt as if he had his full senses about him, and he instinctively had a bad feeling about the woman up the street. She was dressed in a long black cape for a start, and seemed abnormally tall for a woman, well over Stuart's own considerable height of six foot one. He increased his pace and pushed on through the glacial weather with thoughts of Nancy's cosy bed-sit spurring him on.

The street was (and still is) one of the most secluded in the city centre, and at that time of the morning, on such a night, when most sensible people were snug in bed, it was as silent as the grave. As Stuart battled along through the snowstorm, he noticed that the tall woman had started to glide over towards his side of the street. When he was about twenty feet away from the eerie stranger, Stuart realised that she was far taller than he had originally estimated and was actually nearer seven feet in height. Her hair was pulled up tightly into a bun, which highlighted the bones of her skull in her peculiar elfin face, and her long black dress trailed in the snow as she walked. Although 'walked' is probably the wrong word, because in reality she was gliding along as if she were on hidden castors.

Then, without warning, the lanky woman produced a large carving knife from under her cape. Stuart skidded to a halt, and in one heart-stopping moment the woman in black let out a screeching din, which seemed to fill the entire street and then lunged straight at him. He swore in shock, raised his arm reflexively and then turned to run. His legs felt numb from both fear and the penetrating cold as he attempted to flee from the sinister attacker, and he slipped several times but quickly scrambled back to his feet each time, spurred on by the prospect of a knife in his back at any moment. He headed down Oldham Street, hoping that he would come across a policeman walking his early morning beat, but there wasn't a soul about on that freezing morning.

Upon reaching Renshaw Street, Stuart lost his footing on a glassy kerbstone and fell face-first on to the snow-blanketed pavement. Convinced that he was about to meet his end, he turned, out of breath, to face the terrifying knife woman, but saw only flakes of snow whirling down on to the empty dark street. His heart thumped painfully in his chest and he grabbed hold of a lamppost and pulled himself to his feet. He examined his freezing grazed palm and rubbed it on his trousers, then walked unsteadily home, taking the longest route, via Copperas Hill, just in case he should meet the murderous maniacal woman again.

He reached Kensington chilled to the bone, shivering, not only from of the cold, but mainly because of his almost fatal brush with a woman whom he now realised most probably must have been some sort of ghost.

Many years ago I received a telephone call about a sighting of the spectral Roscoe Street knife woman whilst at the studios of Radio Merseyside. An Irish tourist, staying at a hotel on Mount Pleasant, phoned in to tell me how, from his hotel window, he had watched the gangly black silhouette of what was obviously a female ghost, prowling about on Roscoe Street and Mount Pleasant after dark in December 1996.

There is no reason to doubt that this ghost is still active today. If you have seen her, or any other ghost for that matter, email me at tom@slemen.com and I will be only too happy to look into the case.

THE LEGEND OF HICKEY THE FIREBOBBY

Children are highly imaginative, so when they sometimes claim to have an acquaintance that we dullard adults cannot see, we tend to describe the invisible companion as an 'imaginary friend'. Yet just because we can't see something, it doesn't mean it isn't there, of course; just think of microbes, microwaves and the wind and the air.

On Christmas Eve, quite a few years ago, five-year-old Meg from Anfield happened to mention an imaginary friend who visited her most days in her playroom, or so she told her mother. When asked what this friend's name was, Meg said, without hesitation, that it was 'Icky'. Her mum coaxed Meg to draw this Icky person and, using a chunky felt-tip pen, Meg drew a childish representation of her imperceptible pal. He had a thick black moustache, a strange dark jacket and a big yellow hat of some kind. Meg said his hat was made of something which looked just like the bucket that grandma put her coal in; in other words, Icky wore a brass helmet. Meg's mum said he sounded like a fireman, and her daughter became excited and exclaimed, "He is, mummy. He puts out fires!"

When the strange story of Meg's imaginary firefighter reached the ears of her grandma, she was flabbergasted, for she knew an intriguing tale regarding such a person, and it had taken place in the very house where Meg lived – Abbey Road in Anfield.

At the aforementioned abode, at the turn of the nineteenth century, lived Joe Hickey, a forty-four-year-old book-keeper with a debilitating lung condition. Ever since Joe's teenaged years he had dreamed of becoming a fireman, but his fragile health had shattered his ambitions, and instead he was forced to was forced to earn his living as a book-keeper with a meat import firm.

There is an old saying that life begins at forty, and many people are happy to vouch for its validity. Sometimes a person truly finds his or her bearings in life around that age, and may embark on a change in career or lifestyle. This certainly seemed to be the case for Joe Hickey. Some Anfielders thought that the many hours spent pouring over columns of tedious figures had finally caused the middle-aged book-keeper's mind to snap, when he began to dress up as a fireman, regularly donning an authentic tunic, axe and helmet.

But his activities did not stop there. When a gang of young hooligans from Cabbage Hall set fire to an old sawdust-filled mattress in an entry off Breck Road, Hickey, the self-styled 'fire-bobby', put it out single-handedly with a bucket of water and a primitive brass piston-operated fire extinguisher. An unfortunate youth who challenged Hickey's authority to put out the fire received a powerful jet of water in his face, followed by a clout around the ear! Fearing that he was making himself into a figure of fun, Henrietta Hickey tried to talk her unhinged husband out of his bizarre 'hobby', but to no avail, and his activities intensified.

Hickey the Fire-bobby was said to have roamed the streets and back-alleys of Liverpool on most evenings, until the police stepped in and confiscated his dangerous axe. The youths whom Hickey had chased and soaked eventually grew up and told exaggerated tales of the eccentric fireman who would chase them all over the neighbourhood, especially on Guy Fawkes Night. Hickey the Fire-bobby became a bogeyman who joined that dark pantheon of other legendary Lancashire fiends, such as Spring-Heeled Jack, Ginny Greenteeth and the Galosher Man. Eighty-six-year-old Mickey Kavanagh told me many years ago how he had been collared by Hickey at the age of eight, after setting fire to a palliasse in Richmond Row. Mickey was so afraid of him that he struggled free and ran off, leaving Hickey holding his shirt!

THE HAUNTED LORRY

One afternoon, in the mid-1970s, self-employed furniture-removal man Tony Egsby illegally parked his lorry on Bold Street, having been unable to find a space on a meter, and rushed into Lloyd's bank to make a quick withdrawal. He came out five minutes later to behold a surreal sight. About a dozen burly policemen were pushing his lorry up the street. Mr Egsby approached the police sergeant who was conducting the operation, and apologised for having parked on a double-yellow line. The sergeant completely ignored him and instead urged his men to keep pushing. Egsby thought the officer had over-reacted somewhat over a simple parking matter, and he raised his voice to get his attention. "Excuse me there!"

"Yes? What is it?" the sergeant asked, with a look of annoyance on his face. "Can't you see we're extremely busy?"

"I just want to know what you're doing with my lorry."

"*Your* lorry?" said the sergeant uncomprehendingly.

Obviously something didn't stack up and the sergeant craned his neck to look at the offside window of the lorry, expecting to see the driver sitting in his cab, but the cab was completely empty. He immediately instructed his constables to stop pushing and then cautiously opened the lorry's offside door to make sure that no one was hiding inside.

Even before that day, Tony Egsby had had evidence of some kind of ghost haunting his lorry and he said as much to the sergeant, but he and his officers were very sceptical. Nevertheless, was was certainly a mystery. Scratching his head in disbelief, the sergeant told him that a man who had been sitting in the lorry just a few moments before had asked him and his men for a push. The man had explained, rather frantically, that his wife had gone into labour at Oxford Street Maternity Hospital and he had promised her that he would be there for the birth. The sergeant had offered him a lift but the man had shaken his head and said he couldn't leave the lorry on Bold Street and that it only needed "a slight shove" to get it going.

The policemen had been returning from a false IRA bomb scare on Hanover Street when the lorry driver flagged them down. The sergeant simply could not accept this supernatural explanation for the driver's disappearance and looked again inside Tony Egsby's lorry without finding the dark-haired man who had asked for help. The sergeant and his men eventually left Tony Egsby in Bold Street with his lorry and headed back to the station truly mystified.

Mr Egsby had only owned the lorry for five months but already he had had his fill of the supernatural goings-on associated with it. He questioned the man who had sold him the lorry but he claimed to know nothing about its 'other' driver. However, there were rumours that a man called Ryan had died of natural causes in the vehicle, whilst on his way to join his wife who was giving birth three years before.

A month before the Bold Street incident, Mr Egsby had parked his lorry on Muirhead Avenue in Clubmoor, whilst he and a friend delivered a fridge to an elderly woman's home. When the two men came out of the house, they found the lorry moving off along Muirhead Avenue – with no one at the wheel! Tony Egsby's friend ran alongside the runaway lorry and tried to jump up into the vehicle, but without success. Fortunately the vehicle eventually slowed down of its own accord and came to a halt just yards from a busy junction.

In the end, Tony Egsby could not cope with such weird goings-on and sold the haunted lorry at the earliest opportunity. He was glad to be rid of it.

THE GHOST OF GREGORY LANE

On Thursday, Christmas Eve 1964, at 9.15pm, an elderly couple, Mr and Mrs Frazer, of Ormskirk, set out on a journey to the homes of several of their friends on the outskirts of Southport to drop off some gifts. George Frazer's tired old ten-year-old Morris Minor slowly threaded its way through the black slush of the twisting country lanes, which contrasted sharply with the fields on either side which were caked with half a foot of pure white snow. The weathermen had forecast even more snow for that night and a white Christmas to come. Eileen Frazer sat in the front passenger seat beside her husband, holding a batch of Christmas cards made out to six friends, and on the back seats rested the bundle of wrapped presents for the same six people.

As the Morris Minor was wending its way down Gregory Lane, something took place in that car which was to plague the couple for the remainder of their lives. They both heard a grating cough coming from the back seat, and Eileen spun round to find a man a few years older than herself – about seventy – sitting there as large as life. He was wearing a flat cap and a black jacket, and his face was as white as the fields outside. Despite the fact that she had just heard him cough, she could tell that he was dead, both from his skin pallor and the peculiar sunken blackness of his eyes. Mrs Frazer put her hand to her mouth and emitted a stifled cry for help, which startled her husband who was concentrating hard at the wheel in the difficult conditions.

"What is it, love? What's the matter?" George asked. "Is there somebody in the back?"

But Eileen Frazer was so dumbfounded that she could only signal with her eyes that they did indeed have an unwanted passenger. George glanced in his rear view mirror and saw the ghost for himself.

"Oh, my God!" he cried. "Who the heck are you?"

There was no answer, of course, and George swore loudly as he slammed on his brakes and skidded on the dark road, the flakes of the incessant snow drifting in and out of the headlight beams.

Eileen Frazer felt a weakness in her legs and her stomach was up-ended in shock. She clung to George and he held on to her, and they both sat half-turned, speechless and transfixed by their apparently dead unwanted passenger and they nearly jumped out of their skins when he suddenly came back to life. He smiled at them and then picked up one of the gifts lying on the seat beside him and said, "Hmm ... that's all very nice, gifts and the like ... but I see you've left someone out."

Although George was terrified, the man's words also struck a chord, deep within him. Such ghosts are called 'carnates' – they look and even feel solid, and are often mistaken for members of the living. This carnate ghost tapped one of the gift-wrapped presents and again specifically addressing George said, "You're kinder to strangers than you are to your own flesh and blood."

At last, George Frazer managed to conjure up enough courage to reply and ask, "Who are you? What do you want?"

Eileen was now crying hysterically in his arms. "Do something, George! Get rid of him, I'm really scared."

The whole ordeal was like some bad dream, but in this case it was all too real. The ghost's eyes now burned a fiery red, and he thrust a pale pointed finger towards the snow-flecked windscreen and bellowed, "Go down that road, and take the first lane on your left, and if you hurry you might save a woman's life!"

A split-second after delivering this instruction, and he was gone. The gift he had held in his hand fell back on to the seat and George Frazer drove off, babbling incoherently about the Bible, and at the same time trying to soothe his wife's shattered nerves. He chose not to heed the ghost's mysterious instructions, but drove on instead to the home of his friend Tommy Keel. Tommy became quite distressed when the Frazers told him about the ghost in the backseat. He poured them each a much-needed brandy, then knocked back a glass himself.

"Don't go home that way, George," he told his friend, and looked out of the window.

"Why not? You don't think we'll bump into him again, do you? Surely once in a night's enough!"

Eileen clutched his hand as she waited to hear the answer.

"Well, I've heard about that fellow before … enough said!" was Tommy's unsatisfactory reply. Asked to elaborate by George, all Mr Keel would add was, "Nah … enough said."

The Frazers dropped off the other gifts to the rest of their friends, and a few of them said they had also heard stories about the ghost of Gregory Lane, and from what they had heard, he was usually an omen of death, or, slightly more cheerfully, a helper who tried to save people from an impending tragedy.

On the following day, George Frazer answered a knock on their door and found his cousin standing on the step looking very mournful.

"Can I come in, George? I'm afraid I've got some bad news."

It transpired that George's older sister, Margaret, had passed away the night before, at her secluded cottage near Halsall Moss. The fire in her grate had gone out and she had not been well enough to relight it or get herself to bed. She had died alone of hypothermia. Scattered all about her were old photographs of a brother whom she had loved; a brother who had never bothered to visit her for years – George Frazer.

When George heard this he cried out in anguish, realising that the ghost of Gregory Lane had foreseen Margaret's impending death, and had tried to save her by appealing to George. Instead, he, as that poor woman's heartless brother, had chosen to spend most of Christmas Eve giving out gifts to his friends, without a thought for her.

The identity of the ghost in the flat cap is unknown, but from what I am told, he still haunts Gregory Lane, and is mostly active around Christmastime.

THE MONK OF CONISTON

During the course of my work, I am contacted by people from many different walks of life, often with incredible and often quite sinister tales to tell, and the following story was related to me by an elderly man who now lives in Southport.

One evening in the early 1960s, Howard, a self-employed plumber, was slumped in a dark corner of the Casanova Club on London Road bemoaning the fact that his life was devoid of all meaning and pleasure. He had decided that it was high time to kill himself off, metaphorically, that is. He would stop short of resorting to actual suicide, because it was not life as such, that he had had enough of, but the kind of life he was living. He was utterly sick and tired of it, and had decided to walk out of it forever and seek a new one.

He withdrew all the money he had left in the world – a mere thirty-five pounds – from Martin's Bank on Water Street, and hit the road. Compulsive gambling, the wrong types of women and mounting debts, had combined to destroy his old existence, and now it was time to be reincarnated, even if it was only as a vagrant. He had no solid plans as to where he was going to begin this new life; he was like a piece of flotsam or jetsam bobbing about on the ocean currents. First he hitch-hiked north to Blackpool, but out of season in the rain, the resort looked empty and depressing and did nothing to lighten his mood.

So he headed next for Kendal but he found that place equally depressing because it the rain was coming down in buckets there too when he arrived and all the shops were shut. As he mooched about, it seemed to him that every window held cosy scenes of families clustered round a cosy hearth. Such scenes only served to underline his loneliness and he couldn't bear to look at them.

Deciding to abandon the Northwest as a dead loss, he ventured eastwards until his luck finally ran out, and he was left stranded by his lift in the middle of the night in freezing cold torrential rain. In the pitch black he had no means of determining his whereabouts, just that it was utterly bleak, with no visible signs of habitation.

Howard squinted at the pale dial of his Bifora wristwatch and saw that it was 3am. As his eyes gradually grew more accustomed to the darkness, he could make out that he was surrounded on all sides by moorland, broken only by a series of raised grey forms, which turned out to be gigantic limestone boulders. The boulders appeared to have been placed on stone plinths by the hands of giants. Howard crawled under one of these monoliths for shelter, and sat trembling in the cold.

He rummaged blindly in his satchel and located his Ronson lighter, only to find that it was out of petrol. He found a plastic capsule of lighter fuel, bit off its tip and inserted it into the lighter. After the petrol had bled into the wick by capillary action, he pressed the lever, bringing forth a reassuring white flame with a blue heart to light up the darkness. He cupped a hand around it, so grateful for the meagre heat it gave him.

He reached into his satchel again, this time desperately feeling around for something to burn. His hand soon came upon his pocket Bible and he hesitated. What a test of faith – burn its pages and guiltily enjoy the brief warmth, or perish from pneumonia with a clean conscience? Howard dug his free hand further into the bag, and just when the lighter was becoming unbearably hot, his grappling fingers seized a paperback book. "Oh, yes!" he cried to himself jubilantly, pulling out his copy of *Lady Chatterley's Lover*. He let the lighter die for a few moments as he ripped the Penguin book apart with both hands. He crumpled the pages and then twisted the cover into a taper. But now the lighter refused to ignite. Howard swore at it, but it still would not produce its beautiful flame.

As tears of frustration sprang to his eyes, he muttered a rambling prayer to God, and reminded Him of how he had resisted the temptation to burn the Bible. Something supernatural happened. A deep rich voice inside Howard's head exhorted him to, "Believe,

Howard! Have faith!" Howard was inspired by this inner voice, and tried the lighter once again – and this time it produced the welcome flame. He quickly lit the taper, and then touched the scrunched up pages with it. The driving rain was slowing to a drizzle, and a deep silence fell all around. He reclined against one of the plinths supporting the colossal stone above, and decided to burn his spare socks. They smouldered for a while but eventually burst into flames. Desperate to keep the comforting fire going, he finally burned the satchel itself, then dozed off, worn out.

The first thing he saw when he awoke in the grey dawn, still clutching his little Bible, was a heart-warming sight: a tall odd-looking house in the distance, right in the middle of nowhere, ghosted by the morning mists. The fire that had saved his life was now reduced to a small circle of black ash, and Howard moaned as he tried to bring his stiff limbs back to life. He struggled to get up, then walked in a straight line to the house across the moor.

He halted at the door of the house and glanced up at its unique architecture. The building was four-sided and stretched almost a hundred feet into the sky. It was dressed in an out-of-the-ordinary stone that seemed to be studded with glittering gemstones (this was possibly pallasite, a gem-encrusted rock of meteoric origin that has been found in parts of Yorkshire). Nine stained-glass windows, in the Elizabethan style, looked out across the moor from elaborate buttresses, intricately carved quatrefoils and convoluted niches, giving the dwelling the appearance of an ecclesiastical building.

Before Howard could even place his hand on the brass Sphinx-head door-knocker, the oaken door creaked open and two wide-eyed golden-haired boys, aged about twelve, appeared, dressed in smart black suits with jabot collars and laced-trimmed frills down the fronts. They were obviously twins and identical ones at that. Before Howard could begin to explain his predicament, one of them rudely slammed the door in his face. The hungry vagrant tried to twist the great iron handle of the door, but it would not budge. He banged on it with his fist, and then held his ear to it for a response. Inside, the faint high-pitched voices of the twins could be heard, punctuated occasionally by a deep adult voice.

About ten minutes later, the thick weighty door swung inwards once more and a curly raven-haired head popped into view. Judging by his youthful-looking skin, the head's owner was aged about thirty but his brown eyes had an ancient look about them and were unhealthily dark and sunken. He invited Howard to step inside, and in a Cumbrian accent asked him how he had managed to find the house, as they crossed the chessboard-tiled hall. What a ludicrous question, Howard thought; how could anybody possibly miss a house of this size out on the moor? It stuck out like a sore thumb!

"Where exactly is this place, sir?" the Liverpudlian asked, as the tantalising aroma of grilled bacon drifted up his nostrils.

"Oh … somewhere in the Yorkshire Dales," the man replied mysteriously, and steered Howard over to a long dining table where the twins were already seated. A butler with an inhuman, shiny face appeared and served up a plate of gammon and succulent sausages, then went back to the kitchen and brought back a decanter of wine on a tray. His visage was reminiscent of a waxwork mannequin, but Howard voraciously attacked the food despite this observation, occasionally eyeing his mysterious host and the silent twins with suspicion throughout the gorging. By and by his host told Howard that his name was Francis, and that he was a monk from Coniston. Howard didn't give this fact much thought at the time, as he was too concerned with filling his empty belly. Francis added that the twins were Thomas and Patrick Wren, but did not go on to explain whether or not they were related to him.

Whether it was because he was so hungry, or the food itself, that meal was the best that Howard had ever tasted in his life and he carried on eating long after his stomach was full. He would only pause once in a while to glug down a mouthful of the equally delicious wine from his goblet, which was regularly refilled for him by the waxy-faced servant. As he revelled in the sensation of his newly-full stomach and the comfort of his surroundings, Francis told him something that he found difficult to comprehend and made the hairs on the back of his neck stand on end. The monk claimed that he had been born in the reign of Queen Victoria, and that he had discovered a "great secret" on the moor that had extended his life.

Howard gripped the carving knife that was lying on the table and gazed at the fellow in bewilderment. The thought suddenly came to him that the food he had just wolfed down might be drugged or poisoned, and he spat out a piece of chewed sausage on to the plate. Seeing this reaction, Francis smiled good-naturedly and assured him that the food was perfectly safe to eat. Howard was still suspicious and stood up, holding the carving knife out in front of him, as he backed out of the room. Francis shook his head and heaved a deep sigh. There was a look of intense disappointment in his glazed eyes. Howard was not prepared to stay and find out if the look was genuine or not. He grappled with the catch on the door, opened it, and ran out on to the misty moorland.

When he felt he had put sufficient distance between himself and the weird house, he looked back, but could see nothing but a massive boulder, as wide and tall as a house, resting on three long stone legs, just like the one that had afforded him shelter the night before, only greatly magnified. These mysterious structures do exist and are still to be found in certain parts of the Yorkshire Dales.

Howard tramped off over the moors and eventually came to an isolated inn, and used what little money he had left to buy himself a stiff brandy. Sitting by the fire in this remote traveller's rest, was an old man, who lent his ears to Howard's incredible story. That oldster filled his pipe and calmly told Howard that he too had met Francis, a nineteenth century Coniston monk who had discovered an ancient secret buried on the moors. The secret enabled him to create, at will, a house out of thin air, complete with a retinue of ethereal servants, and even permitted him to resurrect two young brothers for company who had died of exposure on the moor when they ran away from home over ninety years ago; they were the Wren boys, and they never grew up into full grown men, but remained as children for evermore.

"That Bible you carried in your pocket saved you from being trapped in that house," the old man told Howard with a knowing look. "Without it you would definitely have been lost forever."

Howard caressed the Holy Book that was still there in his pocket.

"I'm sure you're absolutely right," he said. "And to think I nearly let it go up in flames."

Having found out that the grass was definitely not always greener on the other side of the hill, the Liverpool man hitched his way home to his home city, to find that he had hardly been missed by anyone. What had seemed like a lifetime to him had only, in reality, been a few days. He used the salutary experience to pull himself together and get his life back on track. The 'new' Howard met and married a Southport woman a year afterwards and the couple still live happily in Southport to this day.

Howard no longer feels that his life is not worth living, and he has never dared to venture to that part of the Yorkshire Dales where he was once given food and shelter by the eerie Coniston monk.

THE WITCH OF EDGE LANE

J ust because we live in a modern hi-tech age, where science rules, it is commonly assumed that witchcraft no longer exists; that it is just so much superstitious nonsense once believed in by gullible peasants in days gone by. Let me assure you right now, witches are only too real and are still around today. There may even be one or two females amongst your friends and family who practise witchcraft and who possess remarkable powers, which they may use for good or ill.

Somewhere in the Northwest, for example, there is a strange little house built right in the middle of a central reservation, and an old witch of great repute lives in the oddly-located dwelling. You have probably driven or walked past this quaint witch's house and never given the place a second thought. Anyway, that witch on the elongated traffic island belongs to a family of witches. She has a sister witch in Aigburth, as well as another sister living near Edge Lane, and this story is about the latter.

The Witch of Edge Lane, Clodagh (pronounced 'Clauda'), is a spinster who originally lived in the Grassendale area of Liverpool, but was forced to move out after curious locals began to snoop into her private life, the most notable of these being a judge by the name of Hamilton Gilmour. Although they were neighbours, Gilmour had first met Clodagh one evening at a country ball in Cheshire. The judge took an instant shine to the Liverpool lass, little suspecting her secret profession, and they spent an enjoyable evening together chatting and laughing in between dances.

At the end of the evening, when the musicians were playing the last waltz, Judge Gilmour invited Clodagh to join him in his first-class carriage for the rail journey back to Liverpool, as he had discovered during the course of the evening that, by coincidence, the young lady actually lived in the same street as himself. However, Clodagh politely declined his offer, saying that she had her own means of transport. Imagine the judge's surprise when he reached home on the last night-train and learned that Clodagh had arrived in Grassendale a whole hour before him – without any visible means of transport.

Then there was the matter of the sinister cauldron that had been spotted by neighbours in Clodagh's kitchen, and what about the outlandish-looking female friends of hers who were always seen to congregate at her house on eight specific nights of the year? Those nights were actually the eight sabbats that witches celebrate, and the odd assortment of friends were part of Clodagh's coven.

By the 1960s, Clodagh had become only too aware of the hostility felt towards her by her neighbours, including the judge, and moved to a large but modest house off Edge Lane. Although by now the witch was well into her eighties, she had smooth, unwrinkled skin and looked at least half that age. Unfortunately, it was not long before word got round that she was a witch and she acquired a new set of enemies, the most notable of whom was a security guard who worked at a factory near Binns Road.

Many people who lived near Clodagh remember an incident in the mid-1960s when the security guard went round shooting a number of cats in the neighbourhood with an air-pistol. Unluckily for the guard, one of those cats belonged to Clodagh. She was furious when she found out that her beloved pet had been killed in such a cruel and senseless way and went to confront its murderer. The guard tried to wriggle out of it by denying that he had killed any of the cats, yet he gave the show away rather when, during the course of their meeting, he referred to all felines as vermin.

Clodagh was not to be fooled and immediately cast a bizarre spell on the guard, which caused him to be painfully aware of every blink that his eyelids made, and this strange affliction soon wore him down, both mentally and physically, until he was at his wits' end. Fuelled by a desire for revenge, the guard ended up trying to run Clodagh down in his car, but as he accelerated towards her along Edge Lane late one evening in his Ford Corsair, she pointed her finger at the vehicle and then twisted her hand in one swift movement. At that same instant, the car was seen by many witnesses to overturn and crash, for no apparent reason, since there were no other vehicles involved.

The guard survived, but was now even more determined than ever to wreak his revenge against the witch. As soon as he was sufficiently recovered from his injuries, he stormed round to her house and warned her to watch her back. Clodagh was unfazed by his threats and, fixing him with her eyes, she calmly told him that she was rapidly losing patience with him and that if he made one more threat against her, she would take his life.

Despite the crash, which was widely accepted as being the witch's doing, the guard chose to ignore this warning and slunk off home to think about his next move. It didn't take him long to come up with a plan, and a few days later, he ran past Clodagh's house and hurled a petrol bomb at the window – but it failed to go off. Unsuccessful or not, it was enough to make her carry out her threat, and the guard who had unwisely declared war on the witch was dead within weeks of his petrol-bombing attempt. He was driving in the Welsh countryside when his car overturned and plunged down a thirty-foot ravine – again, no other vehicles were involved!

People in the neighbourhood paid heed to the rumours about the so-called Witch of Edge Lane and not only took pains to avoid her themselves, but also made sure that their children never came into contact with her either.

They say that Clodagh still lives in that same house off Edge Lane – and still only looks forty-something ...

BURNING SECRETS OF PENNY LANE

There is a well-documented poltergeist that is said to have haunted a certain house on Penny Lane since the 1930s, if not earlier, and I have already mentioned this ghost in one of my earlier books. However, Penny Lane has many other supernatural secrets, and what follows is an account of one of these paranormal gems that are to be found in the street that the Beatles made famous around the world.

The 1970s was, in many ways, a rather miserable decade; a time of strikes, electricity shortages, and recurrent discontent in the workplace. In December 1974, thirty-one-year-old John Crandon stood in the middle of a long queue that snaked from Cassidy's Bakery on Liverpool's Kensington High Street, right around the corner. The bread strike was still going strong, and the bachelor was yearning to make himself a toasted sandwich, but he stoically kept his cool, even though people behind him were shoving, pushing and elbowing their way forward, as the files ahead of him inched towards the bakery at a snail's pace.

The chill air of the wintry afternoon seeped through the fabric of his duffle-coat and woollen polo neck jumper and, at the same time, the sub-zero pavement infused its iciness into both of his booted feet. The great billowing clouds above him looked pregnant with snow, and only the occasional tantalising aromas of baked bread, which came floating on invisible wisps through the chilled air, kept him hanging on in the queue. It was only when such essentials were taken away from you, he thought to himself, that you stopped taking them for granted and learned to value them.

Suddenly, out of the afternoon gloom, there came the tinny sounds of music piping. The song was immediately recognisable as the synthesiser intro to 'Gonna Make You A Star' by David Essex, and it was coming from the transistor radio of a twenty-year-old fellow queuer, Deborah Ryan – a girl John had admired from afar for a few years now. She was standing about five places behind him, and was blithely ignoring the repeated requests from two pensioners to turn the radio down. When Deborah noticed John stealing sly glances at her, her eyes lit up and she quickly left her place and sidled up next to him.

"Hi! Pretend I'm your sister ... like I'm with you," she whispered saucily close to John's ear.

His heart pounded. He really did fancy the girl but felt she was much too young for a man his age; but what an opportunity!

"Er ... go on then," he managed to splutter, feeling that all eyes were on him.

"Hey, you! Get back in your place!" shouted a middle-aged man behind them, tapping her angrily on the shoulder.

But before he could protest further to Deborah's queue-jumping, the man broke into a violent fit of coughing, which seemed to really amuse the girl and certainly didn't embarrass or faze her in any way. Other people in the queue also showed their disapproval by tutting and muttering complaints under their breath, but Deborah seemed oblivious to them all and instead turned her attention to her new found 'brother'.

For the next forty-five minutes, Deborah prattled on non-stop about the songs she loved, what she was expecting from her parents for Christmas, what her horoscope had predicted for that week, and how she was going to apply for various exciting jobs in the New Year. The occupations were all of the kind that impressionable girls of her age considered glamorous at that time, and ranged from air hostess to fashion designer.

As John and Deborah waited for their turn to get into the bakery, an old woman came out of another shop nearby called Liptons. She was aged about seventy-five, and she smiled as she said, "You two make a lovely couple, you know".

Deborah blushed, and so did John, and they both smiled uneasily back at the woman, nodding their heads in unison, then sheepishly looked back at one another. For the first time since they had met, Deborah was rendered speechless.

At long last they reached the threshold of F G Cassidy's Baker – just a couple more minutes and they would actually get their hands on some bread and John salivated at the thought of his delicious toasted sandwich. They only just made it in time and were lucky enough to be offered the last two loaves on the shelves. They left the shop together, clutching their precious purchases. There was now no longer any reason to stay together and so John set off in one direction, to his home in Coleridge Street, and Deborah set off in the opposite direction, to her home on Hall Lane.

At 8.40pm. Having consumed his toasted sandwich, which was definitely worth the wait (you only appreciate something when you can't have it), John suddenly felt quite bored, and so decided to pay a visit to his local pub, the Alexandra, on Hall Lane. Even that place was becoming increasingly tiresome; the same old faces and the same old boring tales repeated ad nauseam, but it was better than sitting in moping. As John was sauntering down Kensington High Street, he saw a familiar figure approaching from the opposite direction – it was Deborah, and his heart began to pound.

"Hi! What're you up to?" she asked casually.

"Oh, nothing much. Just off to the local for a pint … nothing better to do."

"Right. I'm off to babysit for my aunt. She lives on Penny Lane. She's having a big night out, so I'll be there till about two in the morning."

"Oh, right … er …Do you need any company at your auntie's at all?" ventured John, amazed at his own forwardness.

Deborah nodded and smiled, "Okay, go on then. It's a long time to be sitting on your own."

They caught the bus to Smithdown Road and walked the rest of the way to the terraced house on Penny Lane. Deborah introduced John to her Aunt Philomena and her seven-year-old cousin Charles. Before she left, Philomena started giving Deborah elaborate instructions about what to do in the event of various different scenarios and emergencies.

"Look, Aunty Phil, I'm not daft, you know. And it's not as though I've not looked after Charles before. You go off and have a good time. Charles'll be fine with us, won't you, Charles?"

"Yeah! Can I stay up and watch the telly for a bit longer, Aunty Debs?"

"No you can't. You should be in bed already. Go upstairs and I'll be up in a minute to read you a story."

So Philomena was finally ushered out of the house at around 9.30pm to go to the party. She had promised to be back at 2am sharp and assured Deborah and John that she would pay for a taxi home to Kensington for them when she got back.

Charles was sound asleep in bed upstairs by 9.45pm, and at 10pm John and Deborah sat down on the sofa to watch the news, with the sound turned down to a whisper, so as not to wake him. John was plucking up the courage to put his arm around Deborah, when they both heard a creaking sound coming from the corner of the room. It was the door hinge and the door was creaking open slowly but steadily.

"Charles?" Deborah said softly to the opening door, imagining that it was her young cousin. "Is that you, Charles?"

There was no reply and the door gently bumped against the armchair as it came to a halt. Deborah looked at John, then got up from the sofa, ready to see who was behind the door. John got up as well, and walked closely behind her as she crossed the parlour floor. The hallway was only lit by the light from the kitchen, and there wasn't a soul there. Deborah ran up the stairs, two at a time, thinking some intruder must have entered the house and had perhaps gone up to Charles's room. John followed her, but thankfully, young Charles was sound asleep and there was no one in any of the rooms.

John tried to rationalise the strange door-opening incident by theorising that it had all been the work of a sudden strong draught blowing through the house, even though he didn't actually believe that explanation himself and nor did Deborah.

Fifteen minutes later, having checked over the whole house, they were sitting on the sofa once again. The spooky incident had broken the ice and they were now laughing about it and embracing one another as they gazed into the fireplace where a coal fire was blazing away. John was in seventh heaven, but this cosy and romantic scene was suddenly interrupted when Deborah noticed something decidedly eerie in that fireplace – all the pieces of coal were of a certain uniform shape, but not like the typical ovoid shape of smokeless fuel. Each of these coals was shaped like a classic eight-sided coffin!

"The coals! Look at the coals!" Deborah screeched.

John shook himself and squinted at the eerie coals in horrified disbelief. "Oh my God! Is this your auntie's idea of a joke?"

As the couple watched, mesmerised, great blood-red flames slowly began to flicker out of the coffin-shaped coals. At the same time, John and Deborah both started to experience painful burning sensations, first in their limbs, and then throughout the rest of their bodies. The searing invisible flames crept upwards towards their faces and John felt ill as his brain registered the sudden intolerable pain. Deborah watched John's normally pallid face redden within seconds, as her own face began to feel as if it too was on fire. She dashed to the kitchen, ran the cold tap in the sink and cupped her hands under it to collect the cooling water. She swilled her face with it repeatedly and the burning sensation temporarily ceased, but then gradually resumed once more, as soon as she stopped doing it.

Through their agony they suddenly heard young Charles screaming upstairs in his bed, and when John, who by this time was groaning with pain, went up to the room followed by Deborah, they found the child writhing in agony on the top of his bed, having kicked off all the covers. His face was mottled with dark purplish-red blotches, and he was sobbing his heart out and calling out pitifully for his mother.

Deborah tried to pick the boy up, but he started kicking and screaming so much that she was unable to get near him. The John tried and managed to calm the boy down sufficiently to be able to pick him up and then carried him downstairs. Deborah opened the front door and rushed outside into the frosty night air, and John, cradling the crying child, followed her. The second they were out of the house all of the stinging, burning sensations abruptly ceased. Deborah reached out for the child in John's arms, and he flung himself into hers, burying his head into her neck. He was still extremely upset, but now he was also shivering in his thin pyjamas, as the bitter cold of the December night air began to bite. The redness on the faces of all three had now completely vanished.

"What the heck's going on?" Deborah asked.

John shook his head and hugged her for reassurance, then gallantly removed his short leather coat and draped it over her shoulders.

"Stay there and look after Charles," he said. "I'm going back in to find out."

"No! Please don't. You don't know what's in there …"

John Crandon cautiously stepped back into the hallway of that house on Penny Lane, and immediately smelt an obnoxious burning smell, and his face began to burn once more. He felt his skin peeling off like the curling pages of a newspaper resting on a blazing fire. He stroked his face in panic, but his fingers quickly established that the effect was all in his mind; his skin was fine. Then there came the greatest shock in John Crandon's life. Standing in the middle of the parlour was a woman. She was dressed from head to foot in black, with a skirt running from her waist to the floor, and she wore a black blouse with a jewelled brooch at the collar. Her brown hair was all swept back and upwards into a tight bun, and that hair was smouldering, as if it were about to burst into flames at any moment.

The outdated woman had large protruding blue eyes, and they were fixed on John with an expression of shock. The woman silently mouthed a word – a word that looked as if it began with an 'O' from the way she rounded her lips. As she did so, a flame shot out from between those lips, as if from a blowtorch, and then was instantly sucked back in, scorching the woman's nose so badly, so that it immediately broke out into blisters the size of a sixpenny piece. Flames then ignited her dress and before John could turn and run away from this shocking, uncanny sight, he saw the flames engulfing the unknown woman's head, curling off layer after layer of charred and sizzling skin and reducing her hair to cinders. The smell of burning flesh and hair was utterly revolting and made John retch.

He had seen and smelt enough. He ran outside and grabbed hold of Deborah, urging her to come away with him. She protested, saying she could not leave the house. What would her aunt think if she came home and found all three of them gone? But John kept pulling her along the pavement with him, away form the cursed house. Charles, who was shivering with shock and cold by this time, began to cry for his mother, and before long, people's faces were appearing behind the twitching net curtains on Penny Lane. Then a small man in his seventies came out of the house next-door-but-one to Aunt Philomena's home.

"Er, what's wrong, kids? Anything I can do?" he asked suspiciously, looking pointedly at little Charles sobbing inconsolably. He recognised the child but did not know either John or Deborah. "Is there something the matter?" he asked again, suspecting that they were abducting the boy.

Deborah explained who she was and then gave a garbled account of everything that had happened in the house. The old man was still not convinced that she was who she claimed she was and asked her exactly which house she was talking about. She told him the number of the house, which seemed to strike a chord. The man nodded several times, his face grave and pensive. Finally satisfied that they were genuine, he invited the couple inside his own home.

"We'd love to but we can't, I'm afraid. My aunt's front door's still wide open," said Deborah. "What if someone goes in and steals all her stuff?"

"Okay, have you got the keys with you? I'll go and lock it for you, if you want," said the old man.

"No, we ran out in such a rush and, anyway, I don't know where my aunt keeps them. We weren't planning on leaving the house until she got home, so we didn't think we'd need them."

"Okay, I'll go and put the door on the catch, then hopefully nobody'll realise it isn't locked. We'll keep an eye on it, anyway."

The old man went over to the evacuated house and returned a couple of moments later. He ushered John and Deborah into his sitting room, where a small mongrel dog with a grey snout growled at them from its place in front of the gas fire. The old man, whose name was Albert, told them that the old dog was perfectly harmless and settled them down in front of the fire. After making them a cup of tea he told them that he had lived on Penny Lane ever since he was a child, and had heard many disturbing rumours about the house where Deborah's aunt lived. Albert had once heard his mother say that a very wicked woman had been found reduced to a heap of charred bones after the Devil himself had risen up from Hell to claim her.

John Crandon shuddered and went numb when he heard Albert's story. Seeing that he had suddenly turned very pale, Albert poured a measure of rum into his tea.

"There you are, lad. Get that down you. I can see you've had a very nasty shock."

He offered the same to Deborah but she declined. He then took a small green-silver-wrapped chocolate novelty from his Christmas tree and handed it to Charles and then continued with his recollections.

"My Aunt Charlotte claimed that the woman who lived there … in your auntie's house, that is … was a Mrs Gardiner. Yes, I'm sure that's what it was. The story went that she had attempted to sacrifice a niece of hers to the Devil, just so he could help her to get this man she was besotted with. I can't exactly remember all the details, but her ghost is still supposed to be seen from time to time in the house, all aflame, apparently. Ooh! The whole thing makes me shudder."

John was desperate to tell Albert that he knew exactly what he was talking about and that he had just witnessed the burning woman for himself. What stopped him was the realisation that, if he did tell him, Deborah would never set foot in that house again. As it was, she had already had enough of a fright. Meanwhile, Albert was going over the whole thing in his mind, trying to dredge up more details about the weird tale from the past.

"Now I come to think about it, the whole thing was supposed to have happened around this time of the year, around Christmastime," he suddenly recalled.

As he reminisced, the strands of a length of scarlet tinsel, entwined in the chain from which the mirror hung above the fire, began to stir. Deborah caught sight of the twinkling movement and almost jumped out of her skin. "Why is that tinsel moving like that?" she asked, nervously, about to grab Charles and run out of Albert's house.

"Oh, that's nothing to worry about that," said Albert. "It's just the heat from the fire making it move. Don't worry, my dear, I can assure you that this house definitely isn't haunted. You're quite safe here."

Albert's account of Mrs Gardiner's body being reduced to ashes sounds to me like an example of 'Spontaneous Human Combustion' – a mysterious phenomenon in which people suddenly burst into flames for no apparent reason. They are then rapidly consumed by a fire that seems to be of an atomic kind, for it has even managed to reduce bone to a fine powder within seconds, something that is difficult to do, even in a crematorium, and after hours of burning. It can take twelve hours of continuous heat at 3,000 degrees Fahrenheit to turn human bones into calcined fragments, but Spontaneous Human Combustion can accomplish that same task inside a minute, and no one knows how this can be possible.

John and Deborah remained in Albert's home until 2.05am that night, when Aunt Philomena finally came home in a taxi. John spotted her through Albert's parlour window, swaying slightly as she walked to her empty house, and he quickly roused Deborah, who was dozing on the sofa next to Charles. They both thanked the hospitable old man profusely for his kindness and said they would have to be going.

When they told Philomena about the awful events that had taken place in her absence, she was extremely sceptical, saying that there story was so ridiculous and far-fetched that they must have imagined it all. However, one year later, she saw something supernatural herself on Christmas Eve, which freaked her out. What that thing was, nobody knows, as she still refuses to discuss it to this day. However, whatever it was, it must have been truly terrible, because it left her so badly shaken, that she and her young son Charles moved out of that jinxed house before Boxing Day, and have never returned since.

CURIOUS CURRENCY

Blood Money

In 1817, a well-used Bank of England five-pound note, that had been exchanged abroad, found its way back to Britain via a French merchant, who had dealings with a Liverpool businessman. At the businessman's counting-house, a cashier was holding the note up to the light to scrutinise its genuineness – as was the usual procedure – when he noticed a series of minute red marks upon the paper. A magnifying glass revealed these marks to be words, a message scrawled in blood, which stated: 'If this note should fall into the hands of John Dean of Longhill, near Carlisle, he will learn thereby that his brother is languishing as a prisoner in Algiers.'

Was it some kind of joke? Or was the writer of the note really a prisoner in Algiers? And if so, how had it got here? Whatever the significance of the note, the cashier thought it best to bring it to the attention of his boss, who felt the note was genuine and took immediate action. Urgent steps were taken by the authorities of Liverpool, the Government, and the joint Foreign Secretaries Lord Castlereagh and Mr Canning, to communicate with Mr Dean and ascertain whether his brother might be being held in a foreign prison. Mr Dean was duly contacted and confirmed that he did indeed have a brother who was missing. Friends and family had long assumed that he had died after a trip to the Mediterranean, and were completely unaware that he had been taken into captivity in Algiers. In fact, he had been held by the ruler of that country for eleven years.

Whilst being held captive, he had been repeatedly forced to do slave labour. He had not been allowed any writing materials, nor any contact with the outside world, so how had he managed to have a message smuggled out? Apparently, he had used a tiny wooden splinter and dipped it in his own blood to write the miniscule message on the five-pound note, which he must have had secreted on his person when he was first captured. Having written his message, he probably used the money itself to bribe one of the guards, or perhaps he gave it to one of the other prisoners on his release.

Surely it was a long shot, a bit like sending a message in a bottle, with only the smallest chance of success, to hope that it would ever reach England, never mind be noticed and brought to his brother's attention. Yet finally it was, but only after many years of being in circulation. A ransom was paid for Mr Dean's release but, alas, too late. He died shortly after his arrival in England, as a result of suffering long-term exposure as a galley-slave for the Dey of Algiers.

Just a Joke?

Another unit of strange currency was placed in the palm of fifty-seven-year-old bargain hunter Hetty Robinson, when she visited a stall at Paddy's Market on Great Homer Street one Saturday in 1997. Hetty bought a big cake for her granddaughter's twelfth birthday, and some jewellery for her daughter.

When she got home, she noticed an unfamiliar coin amongst the change in her purse. It was gold in colour and slightly thinner than a pound coin, but of the same diameter. The profile on the obverse side was unmistakably that of Prince Charles, but he looked much older than he was in real life. The date on the coin, according to Hetty, was either 2020, or 2028, which would place him as King Charles III, and he would be between the ages of seventy-two and eighty. Of course, Charles may never use that title when, or if, he ever becomes monarch, because he could choose to use his 'regnal' names, George, Arthur, or Charles George and Hetty can't remember just what name was displayed on the coin.

She showed the curious currency to a cousin who knew about such things, and his verdict was that it was a sophisticated numismatological joke. Shortly afterwards the coin was lost and has never been found since. So what was on the reverse of the intriguing coin? Hetty vaguely recalls that it was a ring of stars and a map of some country – but not Britain – which deepens the mystery. Was it some private coin-maker's little joke? or did Hetty somehow obtain a coin from some future era?

As far back as the year 2000 there were superstitious rumours doing the rounds about a ten pence coin bearing a small imprint of the Egyptian Ankh, which brought those who possessed it a fortune. However, if the receiver of this coin failed to put it back into circulation, the fortune was sure to be lost. Perhaps someone simply hallmarked a ten-penny piece with an Ankh symbol – or maybe the truth is much more sinister.

Shoebox Legacy

How about haunted money? Well, in the 1960s, Mrs Hall, a seventy-eight-year-old eccentric, died at her home in Wavertree Green. Her next-of-kin was her seventy-two-year-old sister, Lizzie, but when she reached the house she could not find a trace of her dead sister's life-savings. The police were called in but concluded that Mrs Hall must have been robbed some time before she died, perhaps by burglars. Lizzie had other ideas and suspected her light-fingered thirty-five-year-old niece Connie, but nothing could be proved.

A fortnight after the funeral, strange things began to happen at Connie's home. She would hear footsteps on the stairs in the dead of night, and they always came to a halt by her door. One night the door opened, and in the semi-darkness, Connie could see the ghost of her aunt walking towards the wardrobe – where the stolen life-savings had been stashed. Connie screamed out her aunt's name and told her to go back to her grave, but the apparition opened the wardrobe door and began rifling through her greedy and dishonest niece's belongings, looking for the money.

The ghost eventually found what she looking for – a shoebox containing the stolen notes – and walked out of the bedroom with it. Connie was absolutely terrified by the visitation, but she see got out of bed, turned on the light and opened the bedroom door slightly. She could not see the ghost anywhere, but the window on the landing was open and when Connie looked out, she could see a flurry of banknotes from the shoebox fluttering down on to a nearby railway track. She tried to retrieve them but it was too dangerous, and as she picked out several ten and five pound notes from her garden hedge, which bordered the railway embankment fence, there was a terrific shower of hailstones that stung her face and hands.

Only an eighth of the money was ever recovered, and the shoebox in which the savings had been stored, was never found. The ghost of Mrs Hall began to haunt her thieving niece, and even appeared in Connie's dreams. In the end, Connie's nerves became so taut with the supernatural retribution, that she visited a priest and confessed her crime. A few weeks later she also plucked up courage to tell her aunt Joan about the theft, after which the paranormal persecution immediately ceased.

CONSORTING WITH THE DEVIL

IN THE ROSCOE HEAD

In the 1890s, it is said that the Devil had a habit of calling in at the Roscoe Head pub, on Roscoe Street, just around the corner from Leece Street. I first heard of these visits in my old Myrtle Street home during my childhood, many years ago. I thought the story was just a lot of silly scare-mongering in those days; a ploy to get us youngsters to go to church (although I was an altar boy at the time, so I was never far from church anyway). However, the more I have researched into these old tales, the more I have unearthed snippets of information which seem to back up these stories, and today I do wonder if there really is some grain of truth in these hoary old romances and legends.

In the version of the story I was told, the landlord of the Roscoe Head was always referred to as Billy Tonksy, a fictitious surname, surely, I used to think. But no, the Victorian directories and censuses covering that period do indeed confirm that the Roscoe Head Public House, located at Number 24 Roscoe Street, had a landlord by the mane of William Tonks in the 1890s, so the nickname Tonksy is almost certainly right.

The story begins in 1941. A girl who lived in Hope Place, turned fourteen that year, and she and her family attended St Luke's Church, at the top of Bold Street. The girl, Maggie, also attended St Luke's Sunday School, and her little brother Andrew was a pupil at St Luke's Infant School in Colquitt Street. In those days, the church was an amazing sight to behold, with its magnificent stained-glass windows, elegant yellow sandstone and Gothic architecture, and, more importantly, it had a healthy congregation that was daily growing in strength as the church worked to establish itself as the focal point of the local community.

Maggie and Andrew had always loved to stroll in the gardens of the church, especially in the summer, when all the colourful flowers were in bloom. But in the late April of 1941, such thoughts of sunnier times to come were even more important and were used to chase away the dreadful gloom of the Second World War, which hung over everything like a dark shadow in those days of grim expectation, when everyone was living on a knife edge.

On Monday, 28 April 1941, at around 4.15pm, Maggie and Andrew were playing, as usual, outside their home on Hope Place, when a stranger walked by, singing a song that she liked, entitled 'Little Sir Echo', in a mellifluous voice. Maggie was so enthralled by the singing that she did a stupid thing – she stopped playing and started following the man, Pied Piper style, just so that she could listen to the way that he sang that lovely, almost hypnotic song.

The man, who was dressed in a black suit and wore a pristine bowler hat, entered the churchyard and knelt down on one of the pathways there. At this point, Maggie noticed that his shoes looked very queer indeed, for they bent backwards, as their fronts touched the ground, as if the man had no toes. Still singing away, the stranger took out a little wooden box crammed with coloured chalks and began to sketch the church in amazing, almost photographic detail, and at an incredible speed on the smooth stone slabs.

"That's really good," said Maggie, with her arms folded, as she surveyed the excellent chalk sketch.

"Thanks," said the man in an off-hand way, without averting his gaze from his emergent work of art.

"I like really like St Luke's," said Maggie proudly, "I come here every Sunday with my brother and my mum and dad. Do you go to church?" she asked, innocently.

"Not in a million years!" he grunted, his voice seething with irritation ... and something worse ... something which made Maggie suddenly remember her mother's dire warnings about speaking to strangers. Yet, for some reason, she felt compelled to continue with the one-sided conversation.

"Why ever not?" she asked.

"Never you mind," snapped the tetchy pavement artist, selecting out some yellow and red chalks from his box. He then began to wildly scrape flames on to the picture, leaping from the church roof and out of the windows.

"Ah! You've ruined it! It was really beautiful and now you've ruined it!" gasped Maggie, and she ran away out of the garden and didn't stop running until she reached her house on Hope Place.

She told her grandfather about the talented but obnoxious artist. He was visibly shaken by the tale; his mouth trembled and he tried to speak, but the words just wouldn't come forth. Maggie's mother was furious at the way her daughter had followed a complete stranger into the churchyard, after all she had drummed into her. Anything could have happened, and she gave her a severe scolding and sent her to bed without any supper. However, she certainly did not attach any proper significance to the content of Maggie's peculiar tale – until after a shocking incident that took place a week later, on the night of Monday 5 May, 1941.

On that terrible night in Liverpool's history, St Luke's Church became yet another victim of the May Blitz, which ripped the heart out of the city and devastated its people. The church received a direct hit from an incendiary bomb dropped by a Nazi bomber plane. Fire fighters and relief workers were already more than overstretched elsewhere, and there was nothing anyone could do but watch as the inferno raged through the insides of St Luke's Church, destroying everything in its path.

In the early hours of the morning, the death knell of the church was literally sounded, as its enormous iron bell came crashing down from its moorings in the flaming tower. A low cavernous metallic groan reverberated through the ground for quite some distance, as the bell hit the ground. The crack of doom reverberated through air-raid shelters and cellars as far away as Hanover Street and Crown Street, bringing yet more terror to those sheltering within.

Weird rumours then began to surface of a man in black who was seen skipping along Leece Street, howling with laughter as the church burned that night. All around, ARP wardens, firefighters, Home Guard soldiers and 'ack-ack' anti-aircraft gunners, were putting their lives in grave danger carrying out their perilous duties, while this demented clown was running around the precincts of the blazing church, perfectly oblivious to the danger in which he was putting himself, and seemingly actually revelling in the destruction going on on all sides. He sustained not a single scratch, and seemed to vanish into thin air on Roscoe Street, as an air-raid warden attempted to apprehend him.

Upon the following morning, a sad and eerie silence fell upon the parish of St Luke's. Acrid fumes still hung in the air, and plumes of smoke drifted up from the rubble in the nave of the church. In the aftermath, people expected to see the church crumble in on itself, because all of its timber supports had been burnt to ash, and also because the heat of such a ferocious fire normally buckles walls and causes them to collapse. Because of the danger, the Home Guard erected barricades around the smoking shell of the place of worship, deeming it to be structurally unsafe.

People who had belonged to the burnt-out church's congregation wept openly when they saw the sorry state of their church. However, as the days went by and the church and her tower were still standing, they gradually became cautiously optimistic. Surely the church must be capable of being rebuilt if the shell was still sound? This optimism was dashed, two years later, when there came the dire news from the architect who had been commissioned to survey the church, that the damage sustained by St Luke's had been too great and so it could therefore never be rebuilt.

After Maggie had gone to bed one night in May 1941, just days after the church was blitzed, she heard her mother, grandfather and uncle speaking in hushed tones downstairs in the living room; a sure sign that they were talking about something interesting. The girl crept down the stairs, put her ear to the door and listened in on their conversation. She later regretted this eavesdropping, because she overheard her grandfather saying that the man who had drawn those pavement pictures of St Luke's ablaze, and the idiot who had been seen dancing around the church on the night it was hit by a bomb, were one and the same person – the Devil!

This really frightened Maggie because she had actually talked to the man. She went over the whole episode again in her mind and now realised why the toes of his shoes had bent inwards as he knelt down – it was obviously because he had hooves inside them! Although she was frightened out of her wits, as she listened to the adult conversation in that dark hallway, she could not tear herself away from the keyhole. She heard her grandfather telling of his own meetings with 'Old Nick', as he called Satan, and within minutes the girl had burst into tears and was discovered outside the living room door by her mother.

Maggie is in her eighties now, and she has related to me some of the stories which her grandfather, Edwin, told her when she was old enough to understand such strange things. Apparently, he was a regular at the Roscoe Head pub when he was in his late twenties, which was in the mid-to-late 1890s. The landlord of the public house, Billy Tonks, known locally as 'Tonksy', harboured some dark secret, known only to a few, about something terrible he had done early in his life, and he was convinced that he would literally have the Devil to pay for his sins one day.

Edwin, or Eddy as he was known at that time, was a plasterer by trade and his employers were located on Roscoe Street, so the pub was very convenient for him after work, especially on pay day. One hot afternoon, a tall stranger walked into the Roscoe Head, and immediately his appearance caused Tonksy some anxiety. The man wore a bowler hat and an unusually long coat that dangled below his ankles. The most noticeable thing about him was that the pub floorboards vibrated as he walked, as if he was wearing boots or clogs made of iron.

He clunked his way up to the bar and gruffly demanded a large measure of gin. He was duly given one, but made no attempt to pay. As Tonksy was badgering him for the money, the customer knocked back the gin, which hissed loudly in his mouth and throat, as if the spirit had been poured into a searing hot pan. George Ryder, a painter from Everton who had been decorating the pub at the time, was also witness to this extraordinary incident. Having drained his glass, the bowler-hatted customer then slammed it down on the bar and smiled lop-sidedly, although it was more like a sneer than a smile, and then opened his mouth. Steam hissed out from between his teeth. Tonksy's suspicions had been well founded, after all, and he recoiled from the stranger and reached under the counter for his silver crucifix. He thrust the cross towards the stranger and then it was his turn to recoil and he rapidly clumped his way back out of the pub.

Eddy and the painter peeped out into Roscoe Street just moments later, but saw and heard nobody. Then an old woman grabbed everyone's attention by pointing down at the floorboards.

"What do you make of these?" she asked.

There, for all to see, were two trails of U-shaped indentations going across the wood, unmistakeably made by cloven feet. All the customers exchanged knowing looks. Looks that spelt fear. The talk, for the rest of that afternoon, was all centred on the tall dark stranger. They all agreed that, improbable though it might have seemed, they had just come face to face with the Devil.

Living in mortal fear of meeting the Devil again, Tonksy sought reassurance from the Reverend Madden of St Luke's Church and told him all about the demonic visitor. The holy man was unwilling to accept that the stranger had actually been the Devil and tried to persuade the landlord that the incident had probably all been the work of a prankster; someone who knew of his nervous disposition. Tonksy was unconvinced and felt that he had been fobbed off by the priest. He knew exactly what he had seen; there was no doubt in his mind. A measure of his conviction was that he attended the church service at 11am each morning for several weeks, hoping that this would serve to provide him with some protection from the evil forces that he knew were at work in his pub.

A few months later, long after closing time, the topic in the Roscoe Head turned once again to the eternally fascinating subject of the supernatural, and although the landlord tried to change the subject, which he said made him feel very uncomfortable, his tarrying customers would keep on returning to the same theme. An old saddler by the name of Wilson was particularly enthusiastic and insisted on telling a spooky tale that was to give Tonksy a sleepless night that night. Before the glowing blood-orange-red coals of the parlour fire, Wilson related his story to the gathered regulars, who provided him with a willing audience.

Long ago, when he was but thirty-two years old, he had had a bachelor friend called Henry Davis, a man who was never short of money, thanks to a small legacy that he had received. Henry fell in love with sixteen-year-old Wigan girl, Jane Williams, who worked as a servant in one of the large houses on Duke Street. And it was at a local tavern, not far from the Roscoe Head, where Henry foolishly declared, to a group of men propping up the bar, that he would give everything, every penny of his legacy, and even his soul, if he could be the same age as Jane again – sweet sixteen.

As soon as he had finished speaking, a stranger in a long cape appeared in the pub's parlour, and informed Henry Davis that he was the Devil. Without any introductory palaver or wheedling of any kind, he said that he would most willingly grant him his wish to be the same age as the beautiful Jane Williams – but the favour would come at a rather high price – his soul! Almost an hour passed that day as Henry deliberated long and hard as to whether his love for Jane was worth the loss of his soul. Unable to make up his own mind, he foolishly resorted to asking the Devil for advice, and he told him, "You wouldn't even miss your soul Henry. What is it, anyway. You can't see it or feel it, and most people would tell you that it is but a ghost."

"Yes ... well ... I suppose when you put it like that ... Let me think very carefully about this, before I decide. I'm worried about what I might be getting myself into." Again, Henry frowned and scratched his head in consternation. "Okay then why not? ... Yes, I'll do it!" Henry replied. "But only if you can guarantee to make my age the same as Jane Williams's!"

"Oh, I can certainly do that!" laughed the Old Wicked One and slapped him on the back ... just a little too roughly.

"Then take it!"

"Thank you, sir, I will be only too delighted to be of service to you!" said the Devil, and then vanished instantly.

Henry Davis stood there, in the middle of the bar, as lifeless as a scarecrow. He never spoke another word in his life from that day forward. Far from being rejuvenated, as he had hoped, the life seemed to have been sucked out of him and he seemed to shrink and shrivel up from that moment onwards. His life was effectively over and he died just weeks later, from lack of eating and drinking, for he never even had the urge to sustain himself after his meeting with the Devil.

Having watched his friend wither away in such a dramatic fashion, Wilson then began to ponder what other mischief the Devil had done. Had he perhaps aged Jane Williams so that she was now thirty-two-years old, instead of sixteen, thereby carrying out his promise by making Henry's age the same as hers, as stipulated? Luckily for her, this was not the case, and it transpired that, coincidentally, there was another Jane Williams, aged thirty-two, who had lived in the next street to poor Henry. She must have been the Jane to whom the Devil was referring. The Devil had not had to do anything, except take poor Henry's soul, and with it his will to live.

After hearing Wilson's story, Tonksy poured himself a triple brandy and started swigging it down to steady his nerves. He coughed to clear his throat, banged on the bar and announced, "That's quite enough of that subject for one night! I'll have no more talk of *Him* in my pub at this hour, if you don't mind. Now could you all go on home to your beds. Come on, off you go!"

But William John Long, a huge bald muscular man and a blacksmith from Toxteth Park, was thoroughly enjoying the spooky story-telling session and chose to ignore the landlord's pleas, and encouraged the others to follow suit. When he had got everybody's attention, he began telling his own devilish tale. The enthralled late-night customers moved in closer as he started to speak, and Tonksy could not believe his ears when the blacksmith began: "My uncle used to live in McCartney Court, off Roscoe Lane, and he worked in the livery stables next door to this alehouse we're all sitting in now. Anyway, my uncle had two friends, Taffy Whitfield, who was a sailmaker, and Benny Smith, who was a cooper, and they often went drinking together.

Both of them were in the Richmond Street Tavern one afternoon, when a well-dressed man approached them and told them both that they looked coarse and unkempt. Taffy and Benny thought he was making fun of their scruffy workclothes at first, and took exception to his rude comments. But then the man went on to explain that he was a hairdresser from Redcross Street, and as he had just come into a fortune from a successful business venture, he was feeling very generous and charitable. The barber – who gave his name as Jabez Carter, plied the men with drinks and bought them a meal and then invited them to his premises at Number 32 Redcross Street – for a free shave and haircut. Benny Smith was almost completely bald, but Mr Carter winked at him and promised that he knew of a closely-guarded secret which could cause new hair to grow on even the baldest of pates. The barber had already gained their trust with his generosity and they both willingly agreed to go along with the next part of the unelicited bonanza.

However, as the men made themselves comfortable in the barber's chairs, doubts began to creep in. They both wondered why Carter was being so kind to them. Nobody ever gave anybody anything for nothing in their experience, especially when they were complete strangers. So they both felt just a little bit edgy. Then Benny spotted something that chilled him to the marrow; the hairdresser was just about to start cutting Taffy's hair, when he accidentally dropped his scissors. Benny watched as he picked them up from the floor and noticed that their so-called barber friend had cloven feet!

Benny stifled a yelp and shot out of the chair, quickly drawing Taffy's attention to the tell-tale disfigurement. The barber gave a chuckle and told the customers to be calm; they were in safe hands. Unconvinced, Benny desperately tried to drag Taffy from the barber's shop, but his friend was too fascinated to leave.

"Calm down, Benny," said Taffy, "I really do think Mr Carter can bring back your hair. It's worth a try, anyhow."

"Yes, sir, I certainly can, and I can do much, much more ... for a small price," said the diabolical 'hairdresser'.

"Taffy, let's get out of here ... Now!" said Benny through gritted teeth, and he grabbed Taffy's elbow and tried to yank him to the door.

"What kind of price are you talking about?" asked Taffy, unable to resist the prospect of having any he wanted.

"Well, let's see now," said Mr Carter, smiling, and he placed his palms together, as if praying; something which, of course, was unthinkable for him. He eventually wiggled opposing fingers and said, casually, "Your souls, of course. What else?"

That should have sounded all the alarm bells and sent them hurtling out of the shop, but instead, Taffy took the bait.

"Are you trying to tell us that you can grant us anything ... in return for ... our souls?" he asked, relishing all those promised possibilities.

The temptation was just too great to resist.

The two men felt the effects of the drink invading their minds. They felt slightly groggy and detached from the situation, and even Benny's judgement suddenly became clouded.

"How much hair do you want?" asked the barber, playfully, laying his cold hand on Benny's bald head. When he lifted his palm, there was a hand-shaped patch of bristly black hair on the top of his scalp.

Benny recoiled from his touch; there was something deeply unpleasant about it, even evil, yet he felt the hair tufting on his head and it made him feel ten years younger. Hair again! What bliss! It had been a very long time since he had enjoyed that sensation and his vanity blossomed and adversely affected his judgement. He seriously began to debate with himself whether it might be worth losing his soul for a head of thick lustrous hair ... Perhaps this 'Mr Carter' fellow would also be able to get him out of debt ...

A moment later the hair had vanished from Benny's scalp, leaving it bare and shiny once more, like a new-laid egg.

"Very impressive, mate, but can you make this black again?" asked Taffy, pointing to his long grey walrus moustache.

"Of course, anything you want, but let us first come to an arrangement."

The barber's false smile suddenly evaporated and he fixed his victims with his steely grey eyes which had a hypnotic effect on his intended victims. He was reeling them in like fish on a line.

Indeed, the two friends were well and truly hooked. Benny Smith asked for two wishes to be granted: a full head of hair and all his debts to be cleared. Taffy Whitfield asked for three wishes to be granted, on the surface more sensible and ambitious ones: to be loved by women, to have all the money he wanted, just by requesting it, and, of course, to live forever!

Unfortunately, the wishes were not granted in quite the same way that they expected them to be. As soon as he had made his request, Benny was instantly blinded, as the hair on the top of his head, as well as his beard, started growing in such profusion, that in seconds his eyes were completely covered by a thick impenetrable mop. Mountains of bushy grey hair kept on sprouting from the sides and rear of his head, from his ears and nose and eyebrows, and finally from his bald patch, which was soon covered with greasy lank strands of hair. The result not only blinded the poor fellow, but also turned him into a hirsute freak.

"So! That's your full head of hair, and you'll never *see* another bill for the rest of your life!" guffawed his tormentor, delighted with his malicious deception.

Benny cried out in despair, frantically tugging at the masses of unwanted hair which would not only obscure his vision for the rest of his days, but also make it difficult for him to breathe, eat or drink.

Taffy Whitefield had witnessed all of this with such a feeling of dread that he had soiled his trousers, for he now realised, only too clearly, what fools they had been and that, of course, their Mr Carter was none other than the Devil and obviously he would not play fair with him either.

Having finished with Benny, the Devil then swivelled round and focused his attention on Taffy. As he narrowed those wicked steely grey eyes, Taffy felt his body undergoing the most dramatic and excruciatingly painful changes. It began to twist and contort and then shrink, until, within no more than a few seconds, it had been transformed from its human form into that of a domestic cat.

"Voila! You are now immortal, my friend," sneered the Devil, "just as you requested. Oh, and by the way, don't worry about that lovely sleek new body of yours, it's a well known fact that all women adore cats! That *is* what you wanted, isn't it? And should you require any of that money you're so fond of, all you have to do is ask!" cackled the Old Trickster, knowing full well that Taffy, now transformed into a cat, would never be able to speak again.

The motley collection of drinkers in the Roscoe Head gasped as William John Long revealed the fate of the two greedy vain men.

"And that's not all ..." continued the blacksmith, enjoying the reaction he was getting from his listeners, and deciding to milk it for all it was worth. "Even today a strange old cat with a white moustache is often seen prowling about the streets of Liverpool."

"Absolute nonsense!" declared Billy Tonksy, but in a voice that lacked conviction and betrayed his inner nervousness. "If you believe that, you'll believe anything. Come on now, it's time to be going! I'm sure you've all got homes to go to, and jobs in the morning, and I for one need my beauty sleep."

The customers were all beginning to drain the last dregs of their drinks, ready to depart, when an old woman suddenly let out an ear-splitting scream, startling everyone out of their skin. She was pointing to an empty fireside chair, where one of the drinkers, a friend of hers, had been sitting draining his glass of stout just seconds earlier.

"Where on earth's he gone to?" she asked. "I've just turned my back to put my drink on the bar and he's vanished."

The landlord still hadn't unlocked the door, so her drinking partner could not have got out that way. And as the customers checked the toilets to see if he was there, the silence in the parlour was chillingly punctuated by echoing laughter, coming from somewhere inside the pub's chimney ...

After listening to the creepy ghost stories, the customers were already very jumpy and this latest scare tipped them over the edge. They stampeded for the door in a mad scramble and demanded to be let out at once by the landlord. Soon the unfortunate Bill Tonksy was left alone to lock up his pub and to spend the night there in company with its devils and demons.

Unfortunately, the story at this point becomes rather cloudy and the dark secret of the landlord, and his fate, remain unknown, although they say that you-know-who still occasionally visits the Roscoe Head ... So perhaps if you're in town some day, and you're feeling particularly brave, you should visit the pub, perhaps as twilight is creeping along the narrow street ...

OTHER TITLES BY TOM SLEMEN